WORK OF R.E.

IN THE

EUROPEAN WAR, 1914–19

CAMOUFLAGE
SERVICE

The Naval & Military Press Ltd

Reproduced by kind permission of the Central Library,
Royal Military Academy, Sandhurst

CONTENTS.

LIST OF ILLUSTRATIONS.

Chapter I.

ORGANIZATION.

1. First French Experiments.

THE art of Camouflage, as applied to War, is as old as history, but the credit of actually organizing a department to apply the art in the field scientifically belongs to the French.

At Toul, in September, 1914, Guirand de Scevola, a French artist, serving in the ranks of the French artillery, conceived the idea of concealing the guns of his battery by using sheets of painted canvas ; hitherto branches, etc., had been employed. The first essays were primitive and not altogether successful, but he was encouraged to persist, and was allowed to select other artists to help him.

The idea of making and painting suits for the use of patrols, etc., was also pursued.

On February 12th, 1915, a small detachment, the Headquarters of which were at Amiens, was formed to carry on experiments, chiefly in the zone of the 2nd French Army in Picardy. Rapid progress was made, particularly in the direction of camouflaged observation posts, the first of which, a tree, was erected in the neighbourhood of Lihons in May, 1915.

The success which attended the work of this detachment led to further detachments and workshops being constituted at Chalons (August, 1915) and Nancy (September, 1915).

From this time onwards the growth was rapid ; further Base and Army detachments were formed, and the whole Camouflage Service was placed under the command of Guirand de Scevola.

Photos (i) to (iv) show two well-known and typical examples of French work.

2. Origins of British Service.

The idea of forming a Camouflage Section in the British Expeditionary Force was first mooted at G.H.Q. in the winter of 1915, as a result of the success attending the work of the French *Section de Camouflage*, whose workshop in Amiens was visited by British officers.

A professional artist, Mr. Solomon J. Solomon, R.A., was invited to come out to France and investigate the question. The result of his visit was that volunteers from the troops in France were called for. Certain trades, special to theatrical work, such as scenic artists, carpenters, cardboard-workers, etc., were specified. In January, 1916, these men began to assemble at St. Omer under an officer, and five artists (officers) and a civilian stage carpenter arrived from England.

The Headquarters were at St. Omer temporarily, until a building, which had been acquired near Wimereux, should be ready for occupation.

A small party of men was sent to Amiens to be instructed at the French workshop, and the remainder moved up to Poperinghe to become acquainted with local conditions, and make reconnaissances.

In February, 1916, the Poperinghe party moved into the new Headquarters at Wimereux, and was joined by a party of seven French camoufleurs, who had been kindly lent by the Head of the French Camouflage Service for instructional purposes. This party consisted of men who were experts in all the different phases of camouflage work, reconnaissance, execution and erection.

The original plans for the equipment and lay-out of the factory at Wimereux were furnished by the French.

3. First Establishments.

A proposed establishment for the Special Works Park (the title adopted for the British Camouflage Section) was submitted to the War Office and authorized on 22nd March, 1916 (Table I). This establishment included men of special trades, such as artists and sculptors, besides the ordinary R.E. trades. In subsequent increases a very small proportion of artists was included. The artists were rated for Engineer Pay as painters, and the sculptors as plasterers.

Capt. F. J. C. Wyatt, R.E., was placed in command ; and Mr. (temp. Lieut.-Colonel, R.E.) Solomon, who shortly afterwards returned to England, was nominated as technical adviser.

Camouflage work was carried out for the First and Second Armies (Northern Area) from Wimereux ; officers and personnel going up to the front and returning on completion.

Similarly work was executed at the French workshops in Amiens for the Third and Fourth Armies (Southern Area), three more French camoufleurs being attached for the purpose.

It should be noted that only one British officer had any experience whatever of the line, all the remainder had been commissioned direct from England.

Towards the end of April, 1916, a suitable building was hired in Amiens and the British detachment moved in and started to work independently, three French camoufleurs remaining with them to assist.

A substantial increase of establishment was granted in June, 1916, viz., 5 officers, 73 other ranks, R.E.

4. EARLY WORK.

The chief work, so far, was the construction and erection of observation posts (tree and parapet). The concealment of guns was hardly attempted beyond the occasional painting of the guns themselves. Towards the end of May orders begon to come in for gun covers, chiefly painted canvas. In June, 1916, the idea of using wire-netting, garnished with some substitute for grass, was adopted, and a few French women (about 30) were taken on at Wimereux for the work. The experiment proved successful, and the nunber was increased.

The first order for concealing a concentration of guns was received on the 25th June, 1916, for guns in the neighbourhood of Arras supporting the attack on the Somme, which opened on July 1st. The order, which was carried out entirely in painted canvas in the course of one day, amounted to about 3,500 square yards, for 24 guns. At the time this was regarded as a colossal order. Every officer and man at Wimereux took a hand in it, and the work was completed in 14 hours. The determining factor was the sewing of the canvas sheets, which involved nearly one mile of stitching. Only one man knew how to use the treadle sewing machine, and he worked throughout the 14 hours with very brief intervals for rest and refreshment. Under the circumstances neither labour, material, nor experience were sufficient for carrying out the order in wire-netting camouflage, the output of which was only about 100 square yards a day (not enough for one 18-pdr.).

The French camoufleurs returned to their own section in July, 1916, and were subsequently decorated by H.M. the King, at Fourth Army Headquarters in August, 1916, with one D.S.O. and five M.C.s. Later, a D.C.M. was also awarded.

5. INCREASE OF ESTABLISHMENT.

From this time onwards demands began to increase. It soon became obvious that Wimereux was much too far from the front (an average of 60 miles). Officers had to be sent up every day to carry out reconnaissances, often returning the same day. The completed work was sent up to the front by lorry.

A proposal for a further increase of establishment was put up, the basis of which was a parent factory at Wimereux for standard and heavy work, observation posts, etc., and two Detachments, Northern and Southern (each under command of a captain), situated at about the distance of Army Headquarters from the front.

This proposal was eventually approved by War Office on 25.11.16 —Increase 13 officers, 159 O.R., R.E., 3 cars, 3 box-cars, 2 side-cars.

Amiens remained the headquarters of the Southern Special Works Park, and Aire, where a factory was opened on 8.11.16, became the Northern Special Works Park. Female labour (French), was extensively employed. The officers commanding were authorized to accept orders, and to act in every way as unit commanders.

This system remained in force till June, 1918, with certain alterations of establishment in May, 1917, and March, 1918 :—

May Increase— 2 officers, 2 motor-cycles.
March   ,,   —28   ,,   33 O.R., R.E.

6. Depôts in Corps Areas.

The next stage of development was the formation of camouflage depôts in Corps areas, in order to minimize transport by road, and to enable camouflage officers to live near their work, and so keep in closer touch with formations for whom they were working.

This was the inevitable result of the large demands which began in January, 1917, with the preparations for the Arras offensive of April, 1917, and increased continually throughout the summer. The successive preparations for the offensives of June 7th (Messines) and July 31st (Ypres), coupled with the preparations in the Nieuport sector, threw a very heavy strain on the resources of the Park. Three subsidiary factories were formed in June and July, 1917, namely, Wormhoudt, Fifth Army ; Godewaerswelde, Second Army ; Duisans, Third Army, in order to tap new sources of female labour and so supplement the supply of material ; and nearly every Corps had a camouflage officer and depôt. Additional personnel, both officers and men, were found by borrowing indiscriminately from Armies and Corps concerned.

Proposals for a substantial increase, both in personnel and transport, were put forward in August, 1917, but were not approved. The situation as regards transport was particularly bad. Repeated representations were made, but owing to general shortage of mechanical transport, no increase could be granted, and Corps officers were entirely dependent on their Corps for transport, which could seldom be made available.

7. Attachment of American Officers.

In October and November, 1917, the American Army sent officers for attachment, with a view to picking up sufficient knowledge of the work to enable them to start a section of their own. The limited number of officers in the Special Works Park did not admit of any being attached to the American Army for instructional purposes.

8. Section on Italian Front.

In November, 1917, an Expeditionary Force was sent to Italy, and a small camouflage party of 1 officer and 8 other ranks accompanied it. This party subsequently returned in March, 1918.

9. Developments in 1918.

Demands in the early part of 1918 remained at a very high level, partly owing to the fact that additional front was taken over from the French, and partly to the defence lines being constructed in rear of the whole British front. A new subsidiary factory was opened at Noyon in March to supply Fifth Army, but before it could operate the enemy offensive opened, and it had to be abandoned.

In April and May, 1918, an average of 7 officers and 100 other ranks were employed under the Engineer-in-Chief on the construction of defence lines, a work of extreme urgency. Upwards of 130 miles of tracing tape, 5,000 flags and pickets, and 10,000 iron pins were made and supplied by the park for this work.

The results of the enemy offensive brought to light the defects of the over-centralized organization of the Special Works Park, summed up in a letter written by the O.C. to the Engineer-in-Chief on the 26.5.18.

The following proposals were made in this letter :—

(a) A Controller of Camouflage with suitable staff to be added to Establishment of G.H.Q.

(b) An Army camouflage officer to be included in the Establishment of each Army.

(c) A Corps camouflage officer and assistant to be included in the 2nd Echelon of every Corps staff.

(d) One Base Camouflage Factory (R.E.) to be formed to provide personnel for the factory at Wimereux and two subsidiary factories (then at Pont d'Ardres and Rouen).

(e) Four Army Camouflage Factories (R.E.) to be formed for the manufacture of camouflage material in Army areas—these units to be normally allotted one per Army, but to remain transferable in the same way as E. and M. Coys. or Mobile Workshops. The proposed establishments are given in Tables II, IIa, and IIb ; and a comparative statement, showing the changes involved by the introduction of these new establishments, is given in Table IIc.

The proposals were eventually approved on 26.10.18, though they had been actually put into practice in July, as far as was possible.

10. Lessons of the War.

The conditions obtaining in July, 1918, and subsequently, were so different to those of the past two years that it is difficult to make a strict comparison between the new organization and the old. Features common to both were :—

(a) The general lack of knowledge on the subject of camouflage throughout the Armies.

(b) The want of transport on the part of Corps officers.

These disabilities were not removed by the new organization. Steps were being taken to promote education when the Armistice put a temporary end to the necessity, which, however, will always exist in the organization and training of a Regular Army.

It is possible that the final organization was built on too rigid lines, in so far as no straightforward method existed for switching officers and personnel from a quiet sector to the scene of greatest activity and need. This might be remedied by the adoption of a system similar to that of the Special Brigade or Tunnelling Companies, under which Detachments would not be tied to definite Armies, nor officers to Corps.

Another disadvantage is apparent—that of nomenclature. The word *Camouflage*, associated as it is with dead horses, or pantomime, and savouring therefore of mystery and special technique, led, often unconsciously, to the adoption of an apathetic or non-serious attitude towards camoufleurs. However, the word has arrived with every appearance of making a long stay.

11. EDUCATION.

From August, 1916, selected officers were sent to Wimereux from the various Armies for periods of two days' instruction. In all, some 300 officers went through this course.

In addition, parties of officers came down for the day to be shown round, and close touch was maintained with the Army Sniping Schools.

Camouflage officers lectured at Artillery Schools, Machine-Gun Schools, and the R.E. Schools.

During the late summer and autumn of 1917, Artillery Brigade Commanders in the Second and Third Armies spent two days at Wimereux, and two days with the Experimental Section at St. Omer (described in Chapter III, para. 31). The experimental ground there was also visited by the First and Second Army Artillery Schools.

In addition, during the winter of 1917-8, lectures to various formations were given by Corps camouflage officers, and visits were paid to the various exhibition grounds in Corps and Army areas.

In May, 1918, the Officer Commanding the Northern Special Works Park was nominated to command the Camouflage School, England.

This had been started in Kensington Gardens as an exhibition ground in 1916, and for a time was under the control of

Lieut.-Colonel S. J. Solomon. A regular officer was soon appointed, and it became a School.

At first it only received visiting officers for the day ; later, classes were formed of officers from the various commands. The School expanded gradually, and a distinct experimental branch was also formed. Information on all technical subjects was interchanged between the Park in France and the School in England.

Authority was also given for an interchange of officers, in order that the education in England might be kept up to date ; also officers on the staff of the Camouflage School were sent out to France for a fortnight's tour round the Corps depôts.

It was further arranged that reinforcements or replacements of camouflage officers in France could, if necessary, be obtained through the School, where records were kept of all officers who did the course.

After the Armistice the School at Wimereux was made the repository of samples and records of all the work done in France. Later it was removed to England, where shortage of funds put an early end to its existence.

12. FRENCH ORGANIZATION.

The organization of the French section was, broadly, as follows :—

A Headquarters Staff, with eventually an Experimental Section at G.Q.G.
Base Factories.
Army Factories.
Divisional Camouflage Experts.

It is believed that efforts were being made to transfer the whole of the service to the Air Force.

The essential difference between their organization and the British lies in the following :—

(i) *Base Factories.*

They had more Base factories, employing a much larger number of women than we.

These factories were not, as in our case, all under one officer, whose function was to standardize and co-ordinate processes and methods.

(ii) *Army Factories.*

Their functions were :—
(a) To receive material from the Base factories and adapt it to local conditions.
(b) To make the simpler types of O.P.s.
(c) Erection of all O.P.s.
(d) Headquarters of the Divisional Camoufleurs.

H

Women were not, as a rule, employed at these factories.

Each Division had a *Chef d'équipe, i.e.*, a N.C.O., but corresponding to our Corps Officer, with a detachment up to 20 men attached to him from troops in the Division.

He carried out camouflage work of all descriptions on the Divisional front. He always accompanied the Division. In addition there was a *Chef de Secteur*, also Divisional, who did *not* move with the Division.

A fairly large skilled personnel formed part of each Army factory for work in the factory and also for the erection of O.P.s.

The total strength of officers, *Chefs d'équipe* and men was about 1,200, and they employed up to 8,000 women and a large number of prisoners.

They also suffered considerably from lack of sufficient transport, but the French system of pooling all army transport perhaps made the need less acute.

Another disability was the fact that the Divisional camouflage experts, not being officers, were often placed in difficult positions in dealing with officers of artillery, etc. Attempts were being made to have commissions conferred on these *Chefs d'équipe* when the end came.

The great majority of them were artists, architects and decorators. There were few or no engineers among them.

The Base factories had, of course, tradesmen, but no definitely mechanical officers or senior N.C.O.s. Their factories were therefore not scientifically run as regards mechanical processes, though the lay-out in the case of those factories, which were built solely for camouflage purposes, was excellent.

They had, on the other hand, one or two chemists and dyeing experts.

13. AMERICAN ORGANIZATION.

This was divided into :—
1. Shop and Replacement Battalion.
2. Battalion for each Army.

Shop and Replacement Battalion.

This was commanded by a Lieut.-Colonel, who was the Head of the whole Camouflage Service, and was attached to Chief Engineer at G.H.Q.

There was a H.Q. and 2 Companies—the total strength, excluding medical and transport, being 27 officers and 538 other ranks.

Transport: 2 cars, 3 box-cars and 8 lorries.

Their function was production and education, and roughly corresponded to our Base factories.

Army Battalion.

Commanded by a Major—with H.Q. and 2 Companies—total strength, 32 officers and 524 other ranks.

Transport: 1 car, 20 motor-cycles with side-cars, 21 box-cars, 1 lorry, 100 bicycles.

The majority of the personnel were armed with revolvers.

The O.C. corresponded with our Army Camouflage Officer.

Each Corps had a captain and 4 men—each Division, 1 subaltern and 4 men.

In addition, 4 officers and 16 men administered the 4 to 6 dumps in the Army area, which were accessible to Divisions.

The remainder of the personnel was utilized on camouflage work in the Army area for which no particular formation within the Army could be held directly responsible.

Comments.

The American organization was built on the experience gained by our own and the French.

It overshadowed ours in respect of numbers and transport.

In regard to numbers, they were expected to do far more actual erection and forward work than in the British Army; but it must be remembered that they were dealing with troops that were not fully trained.

In the matter of transport they appear to have been well—but not too well—equipped.

14. LIAISON.

From August, 1918, onwards the Heads of all the Allied Camouflage Services met at a monthly conference.

Previous to that, liaison was more or less haphazard, though constant. It never occurred that any section had adopted any innovation without the other sections becoming quickly aware of the details.

Chapter II.

PRODUCTION.

15. Factory Processes.

Throughout the history of the Park the ruling idea was to standardize articles, as far as possible, in order to facilitate quantity production, and to perform every process mechanically if possible. The lack of mechanical officers was a serious handicap. Such as joined from time to time were all sent up the line, as it was considered that the work there was the more important, and the artist element needed a mechanical leaven.

The workshop management was consequently in the hands of comparative amateurs, as the O.C.s Parks were far too busy with administrative work to be able to devote as much time to the subject as it demanded.

Every credit must be given to the O.C.s Northern and Southern Parks for the energy and resource with which they tackled the problem of increased production. Considering the unsuitable premises they occupied, their limited resources, and the continual necessity for visiting persons and places all over a two-Army front, they worked wonders.

A remedy for the last of these difficulties was sought in the new organization (applied in July, 1918), under which factory processes were divorced from advisory work in the Field ; and the immediate results were most encouraging. One factory (Rouen) was particularly progressive, and practically every operation connected with the painting and stripping of canvas was performed mechanically. The other factories were in process of doing the same, and were only waiting for the necessary machinery.

16. Machines.

Each Base factory was equipped with the following machinery :—
Prime mover (either electric, or oil, or steam engine).
1 lathe (5-in.).
1 band saw (Wimereux, 3).
1 drill (up to 1-in. holes).
1 paint grinder (small, for re-grinding waste).
Besides these there were on order for each factory :—
2 paint-spraying machines with air-compressors.
1 grinding machine (36-in.).
1 boiler (500 lbs. at least).

These were exclusive of home-made articles, such as painting and stripping machines, paint-mixers, etc.

The above can be regarded as the minimum requirements of a self-supporting factory, and may require supplementing for particular manufactures. For example, the production of Chinese attack figures involved two additional band-saws at Wimereux.

In addition, a dyeing plant, of a somewhat promiscuous character, was installed at Wimereux. This worked continuously from early 1917, and was always being added to, as the amount of material to be dyed increased. As experiments in dyeing progressed, which were carried out by an officer chemist and an assistant sapper, it was found that some processes, which had been carried out by painting, could be equally well performed, and with greater economy, by dyeing. The termination of hostilities arrived just as arrangements were being made to dye also at Rouen. A good deal of dyeing was carried out, by contract, at Amiens, in the urgent times of 1917. Nevertheless a dyeing equipment was not regarded as an essential for a factory, since the work could be better done in bulk in England.

An absolute essential to every factory was some method of drying their production of canvas strips, nets, etc. This problem was never solved, and proved a most serious handicap. All painted canvas, especially if oil is used in any quantities as a medium, will heat if stacked when wet. There was a constant danger from fire from spontaneous combustion, and continual and elaborate precautions had to be taken to prevent it.

Fortunately, there were never any disastrous results, but the French, from whose misfortune useful lessons were learnt, on one occasion had a whole train burnt, and on another occasion their main painting shop (a large riding school).

A further essential is a large covered floor space where work can be done irrespective of weather. Aeroplane hangars were found ideal for this purpose.

17. CHEMICAL LABORATORY.

An officer chemist was obtained from the Special Brigade in October, 1916, and a laboratory was set up. This was an absolute necessity and did excellent work.

The chief subjects studied were :—

(a) Fireproofing.
(b) Paints.
(c) Paint mediums.
(d) Dyeing.

(a) *Fireproofing.*—This is dealt with in Chapter III, para. 27. The subject was studied with other objects at the instance of the

Director of Works and others, *e.g.*, fireproofing of buildings, tents, curtains, etc. One of the results of this was the installation of a plant (under control of the Q.M.G.) for the recovery of by-products —silicon, water-glass and grease from the waste liquids of the hydrogen factory near Arques. The water-glass was used as a fireproofing agent for wood-work. It was excellent for temporary buildings, but is believed to be unsuitable for permanent work, as it rots wood-work in time.

(*b*) *Paints*.—Efforts were being made to improve the quality of paints, and to analyse the paints that were supplied. Specifications were made governing the composition and shade of the various paints, but they were over-ruled by the hard facts of the case. Certain raw materials were particularly difficult to obtain.

(*c*) *Paint Mediums*.—From the first, water-paints, with a small proportion of oil and large proportion of glue, were adopted, in preference to oil paints, on account of the heating difficulty already alluded to.

Experiments were being continually made to find the most satisfactory all-round medium as regards economy, accessibility, and safety.

A novel medium was tried and adopted, as far as the supply went, in the shape of animal blood, obtained from the local abattoir. This proved very satisfactory.

In the course of research work in this connection it was discovered that, by a very simple process, an excellent substitute for gum or glue for adhesive purposes could be produced at about one-sixth the cost. Considerable quantities of this were supplied to C.O.O., Boulogne, for truck labels.

This substitute was reported to Controller of Salvage and Ordnance, in the summer of 1918, with a view to the possibility of its being adopted universally.

(*d*) *Dyeing*.—Preliminary lack of knowledge on the subject of dyeing led to many mistakes being made, notably the use of green dye to represent grass. In the end a series of dyes had been adopted which gave a very wide range of earth colours. A reliable dye to produce a good grass colour was not found until later, and even then it was doubtful whether it was either obtainable in quantity, or cheaper than paints.

18. STORES.

Stores were obtained from three different sources :—

(1). Vocabulary stores from A.O.D.—three-monthly estimates (*see* Table III).

(2). Building materials and R.E. stores, either locally or from Calais—monthly estimates (*see* Table IV).

(3). Special stores through F.W.5, War Office.

Later, the Director of Engineering Stores provided for (3), a six-monthly estimate being furnished.

The difficulty of obtaining suitable paints has been alluded to. Those provided normally by A.O.D. are designed for the purpose of preserving buildings from the ravages of weather—art is naturally a secondary consideration. They proved very variable in quality, and the specifications were evidently loose. Further, the lack of certain raw materials and the extraordinary and sudden growth of demands, which occurred at most inconvenient periods, *i.e.*, just after the estimate for the ensuing quarter had been submitted, made the supply of paints a difficult matter. Shortages were of constant occurrence, and supplies of very inferior paints had to be accepted in response to urgent supplementary demands.

These were made good, as far as possible, by purchase in France. It was very difficult to frame specifications which manufacturers could be forced to adhere to. It must be added that the wave of " camouflage " enthusiasm which swept over England led to an enormous expenditure of paint and increased the shortage. Buildings of all varieties, which were neither concealable nor in danger of becoming targets, were liberally treated to floods of paint ; the only result of which was often to make them more conspicuous from the air than before.

The problem was in a fair way to solution when hostilities were suspended. Also, steps had been taken in England to put a stop to the indiscriminate painting of factories, etc.

Canvas and Scrim.

These were supplied through A.O.D. to begin with, but the supply was taken over later by D.E.S.

On the whole, the flow of supplies was good. Occasional shortages were made good by purchase in France.

Wire-Netting.

This was at first supplied through the Engineer-in-Chief, and later through D.E.S. At various times there were great shortages. Eventually it was arranged that the Camouflage Parks should have a special allotment, it being specified that all wire-netting of 1½-in. to 3-in. mesh should be taken.

Fish Nets.

These were originally obtained in France, until arrangements had been made for a constant supply from England. It cannot be said that they proved altogether satisfactory. Both Corps camouflage officers and clients preferred them to wire-netting because they were so portable, but they were not durable, and were difficult to erect satisfactorily.

A great advantage in them was that they were much quicker to produce.

Dyes and Special Stores.

Permission was given for certain more or less direct dealing with F.W.5 on the subject of special stores, covering indents being sent in through Engineer-in-Chief.

In summer, 1918, arrangements were concluded for a civilian chemist to be attached to the staff of F.W.5 for the purpose of advising on all chemical questions involved in the purchase of special stores. These embraced paints, dyes, fireproofing.

19. GENERAL OBSERVATIONS.

The growth of a new science under the stress of war conditions was necessarily forced. At every period the main object of the service was to produce *something* that would be just good enough in the shortest time possible. In such circumstances the best results could not be expected, and very much still remains for an Experimental Branch to do. This applies as much to the selection of raw materials as to the execution of practical work. Some idea of the magnitude of the work done during the War may be gained from Tables V to IX.

Table X is a typical Monthly Return from the main factory at Wimereux.

CHAPTER III.

EXECUTION.

20. OBSERVATION POSTS.

IT has already been briefly mentioned in Chapter I that the conceal-ment of observation posts was the chief form of activity up to July, 1916, after which the concealment of gun positions began to assume premier importance.

Observation posts may be classified as :—

> TREES—Direct observation by observer.
> PERISCOPES—Indirect observation.
> PARAPETS—Direct observation.

The principle of all these O.P.s is the same, *i.e.*, the replacement of some existing object, whether tree, brick wall, section of parapet, etc., etc., by an exact external representation (reinforced by interior metal work) which will conceal, and give reasonable protection to, an observer or periscope, behind or inside it.

The copy having been made after careful preliminary reconnais-sance, the original is removed and replaced by the copy during the night.

The reconnaissance was always made by a camouflage officer, and was illustrated by coloured sketches. As the selected object was usually in an exposed situation and under direct enemy view, these reconnaissances presented some difficulty and were generally made at dawn. In only one instance was a photograph taken of the selected object. This was practically valueless, as the light at dawn was too weak.

The next step was, in the case of trees, the construction of a small plaster model, finished in every respect, to enable the copy to be made in the workshops at the Base without the actual presence of the reconnoitring officer.

A few days before completion, excavation drawings, together with a detailed statement of labour and transport, were sent to the formation concerned so that everything might be ready for the final erection by the camouflage personnel.

In practice these excavations were seldom complete, and had to be finished off properly by the erecting party, who had some anxious times on that account from doubt as to whether they would get the erection done before dawn. It is believed their work was never detected by the enemy, though in two particular cases (a tree and a telegraph pole, both accommodating periscopes) the work was within 50 yards of the enemy. About 6 trees (out of 45 erected) were destroyed by enemy shell-fire, whether by design or by accident it is impossible to say.

The actual erection of trees and periscopes was always done by camouflage personnel, also the vast majority of parapet O.P.s. The experiment was tried of handing over parapet O.P.s to units to place for themselves, but this did not prove satisfactory.

A later development in the O.P. industry was the provision of portable O.P.s, armoured or unarmoured, which could be easily carried by an individual and placed anywhere.

21. TREES.

The first tree actually erected by the Special Works Park was reconnoitred, constructed and erected, under the supervision of Lieut.-Colonel Solomon on 11.3.16, i.e., before the actual constitution of the Park (22.3.16). The exterior of the tree was real bark sewn on canvas and came from a willow in the King's park at Windsor. The metal interior was specially designed in London. The external appearance of the tree was perfect, and indistinguishable from the real tree at a few paces. It was erected near Bridge 4 on the canal north of Ypres near Burnt Farm. Being small (only 8 ft. high) and specially constructed, it was easy to handle and was actually carried up and erected in one piece ; it was, of course, quite close to a good lorry road, and a considerable distance from the line. In practice it proved of little use ; it was too small to admit any but a most determined and enthusiastic man, and was too far off for good observation—faults due to inexperience.

Sketches on *Plate* I show the standard metal interior of an O.P. tree. The metal was only bullet-proof as to its front. (Miris steel, ·28-in. thickness, made and supplied by Messrs. Roneo.)

The design was made in March, 1916, and sixty were ordered in England. It was considered, and the decision was justified, that a standard tree interior was necessary if delay in meeting demands was to be avoided. The design proved to be on the small side, but on the whole was thoroughly satisfactory. Its weight was less than half that of the French pattern (which was of $\frac{1}{2}$-inch mild steel, built up in panels, bolted to upright T's) and could be erected in one-third of the time with one-third of the working party.

The French type was used up to July, 1916, until the English ones began to arrive.

In the case of the French type, the erection invariably occupied two nights and sometimes three ; in no case did the British type occupy more than one night.

On the other hand, it should be stated that the French type gave more room to the observer (2 ft. internal diameter), and further that they were unable to get hardened steel.

On the whole, it cannot be said that O.P. trees proved a great success, the chief reason being that the trees selected did not always give observation that was absolutely vital, and which could not be obtained from somewhere else. In short, the principles laid down in S.S. 206—*The Principles and Practice of Camouflage**—were not observed. The consequence was that the excellence of observation did not compensate for the comparative discomfort of the observer. This failure must generally be attributed to the formations concerned, and cannot be laid to the account of the reconnoitring officers, who neither knew the front, nor the artillery needs, and were therefore not in a position to argue the matter. This applies more particularly to the first year of existence of the Camouflage Service.

Practically all the trees that were erected were north of the Bethune–La Bassée road, the country being flat and natural O.P.s rare.

Plate II shows a typical reconnaissance by a camouflage officer for an O.P. in Ploegsteert Wood. *Plate* III is a copy of the plan sent to the unit responsible for doing the preliminary work of excavation, and *Photo* (v) is a back view of the O.P. taken two and a half years after it was erected.

22. PERISCOPES.

The original periscopes used were of French manufacture, 6 ft. 6 in. or 10 ft. long.

Designs for improved periscopes were made in the light of experience gained, and were eventually executed by Messrs. Ross in England. The difficulties of getting lenses, and the congested state of such firms in England as were capable of making periscopes, led to a considerable delay in obtaining them. The eventual 7 ft. 6 in. and 10 ft. 6 in. periscopes made by this firm were excellent.

The conditions which must be fulfilled, if successful use is to eventuate, were described in Section 9 of *The Principles and Practice of Camouflage*, and are, shortly, as follows :—

(*a*) Periscopes can be used in two distinct ways :—

    (i) To obtain command ; or

    (ii) To obtain head cover.

* This pamphlet was issued in France in March, 1918. Sect. 9, pp. 15 and 16, points out among other considerations that " It cannot be expected that a tree will form a comfortable O.P. It is, therefore, only likely to be used if observation on some important target cannot be obtained by any other means. . . ."

(b) In all cases provision in the shape of a lined bore-hole should be made, into which the periscope can be lowered for cleaning purposes, or to protect it when not being used from damage by shell-fire.

(c) Periscopes are optical instruments, and extremely liable to damage or destruction by careless treatment ; cleaning the eye-piece or object glass with any gritty material will damage the lenses irretrievably.

(d) They can be placed in any object which can accommodate an internal tube 4 in. in diameter, such as a tree, telegraph-pole, brick wall, etc.

(e) Reasonably comfortable accommodation can be arranged for the observer, but it is important that concealed access should be provided.

These conditions were usually observed in the case of periscopes, and some most valuable O.P.s were thereby obtained. The work entailed was sometimes very considerable, long tunnelled approaches being frequently made, notably in the case of periscopes installed at Verbranden Molen, The Bluff, and Hill 70.

Erection of three 24-ft. Periscopes at The Bluff.

Plates IV and V illustrate one of the most remarkable works of this description.

These periscopes were erected for the X Corps R.A. and H.A. as artillery observation posts for the Messines battle. The excavation work was started by the 2nd Australian Tunnelling Company, on April 26th, 1917. The drives to the O.P.s were tapped off the 6 ft. × 3 ft. gallery leading to the main underground defence system, the average length of the drives being 50 ft. At the end of the drives, just under the forward lip of the crater (nearest the enemy), a rise of 24 ft. was made, lined with steel tubing on account of the wet condition of the ground. At 24 ft. the tubing was discontinued and a wrought-iron pipe, 10 in. diam., jacked to the surface. This part of the work proved very difficult, as the heavy rain caused the sides of the craters to slide. The pipes had to be withdrawn several times before they were got into a dead vertical position.

The periscopes were fitted so that they could be lowered in case the craters were suddenly shelled ; they were also kept in a lowered position when not in use. The rising and lowering was done by means of pulleys, ropes and counterbalanced weights ; lowering was also necessary for cleaning the top lens. These fittings were made for the purpose at Wimereux.

The first of the periscopes was completed on May 26th, the second on May 29th, and the third on June 2nd. After the excavation was started no breaks occurred, shifts working day and night, the approximate amount of earth moved being 3,852 cubic feet. The tops of the periscopes, which protruded above the ground about 6 in., were covered with a cap made of wire-netting and plaster painted so as to blend in with the colour of the surrounding earth.

Two days after the second periscope was completed, one of our own shells exploded near the pipe, damaging the periscope and knocking the pipe out of the vertical. The periscope was repaired on the spot, and the pipe straightened up at night ; this had to be done from the outside, which necessitated digging down 12 feet by the side of the pipe, and pulling it straight with chain blocks. Owing to heavy enemy shelling and gas, it took two nights to complete.

After the advance all three periscopes were salved in good condition. The lip of the crater where the pipes came out was about 80 yards from the enemy's front line.

Plates VI, VII and VIII show a typical periscope tree—" Choat."

23. PARAPET O.P.s.

These eventually consisted of two main types :—

(a) *The Oliver*, of which the dimensions were governed by the ordinary sniper's plate.

It was impossible to foretell the numbers that might be required, and therefore it was designed to take either a special front with sliding shutters to cover the loophole, or an ordinary sniper's plate.

The front only was armour-piercing bullet-proof, the remainder was merely shrapnel-proof, and large enough to accommodate a single observer with field glasses.

Plate IX illustrates a typical excavation drawing for a parapet O.P. with sandbag or earth front with cabin, Oliver type.

(b) *The Roland* was designed to meet the requirements of sentries only. The front was ordinary bullet-proof, the remainder shrapnel-proof, and the whole was mounted on handles for convenience of transport. It calls for no special comment. (*Plate* X.)

In addition, the Beehive O.P. was supplied to meet the demands of an offensive. It was unarmoured, portable and easily placed.

This is illustrated in *Plate* XI.

Erection of Special Type Observation Post at Bluff Bank.

Occasionally O.P.s of a special type were demanded for special places. *Plates* XII and XIII give details of such a one erected near Hollebeeke. Work was started on June 28th, and completed on July 20th. These observation posts were erected for the X Corps H.A. and R.A.

The excavation work was done by the 175 Tunnelling Company, and consisted of a drive approximately 160 ft. in length, opening out into a chamber 12 ft. × 14 ft. × 6 ft. ; out of this chamber two 3 ft. × 2 ft. box rises were made, which came directly up the centre of two large mounds of earth, the height of the rise being about 14 ft. above the roof of the chamber, and on the top of these rises two steel E type O.P.s were erected and camouflaged in such a way as to blend with the mounds of earth. The total amount of earth moved was 3,804 cub. ft.

The greatest difficulty in this job was met in getting the material to the site, owing to heavy enemy shelling.

The observation posts were about 250 yards from the enemy front line.

24. Chinese Attacks.

Dummy silhouette figures were first made to supply a demand from the 46th Division in May, 1917, for use in a raid. Their purpose on that occasion was to draw fire off the raiding party.

The original 300 supplied were made of 3-ply wood and hand-painted, all the available talent in the park being turned on to the work, which was completed in four days.

The problem of rapid execution was then studied, and eventually they were made of stout millboard, stencilled, and made in ten different types which covered the various attitudes that might be assumed by a man between the lying and upright position. The whole process was carried out by unskilled woman labour, and, in view of the demand that arose, became a standard factory production. Millboard was adopted because 3-ply was unobtainable in sufficient quantity, though the latter would have been much more suitable.

They were used :—

(a) To draw off a real attack.
(b) To test an enemy barrage.
(c) To make the enemy disclose his machine-gun positions and defensive arrangements.
(d) To make him man his parapets and expose himself to shrapnel.

In all these rôles the attack figure proved very successful when properly handled by trained personnel.

Plate XIV shows the general method of fixing and operating dummy figures.

In one Corps during the third battle of Ypres the Corps Cyclist Battalion was specially trained in the use of these figures, and their work proved most useful during the general attacks.

The method of employment was as follows :—

Silhouette figures were carried up the night before the attack, and placed in positions where they would be seen by the enemy directly they were raised. The method of fixing them was as follows :—The base of the figure was held down by means of staples, and a wire run from the head of the figure to another staple immediately in front, this wire being of such length as to allow the figure to be raised just short of the perpendicular. On the back of the figure was hinged a light stay, which was attached by wire to the head of the figure, and to which the operating wire was fastened ; the idea being that, when the operator pulled the figure up, the strain came first on the light stay which rose to the perpendicular, and then on the figure itself. On releasing the strain, the weight of the figure lowered it to the ground again.

As the ground permitted, groups of up to six figures could be operated by one main wire, and by one man.

The fixing and placing in position of the figures had to be carefully done and by men previously instructed in the work.

Examples.—

On July 28th, 1917, three days prior to the Fifth Army attack, a practice barrage was carried out along the whole Army front ; some 300 figures were placed in position and worked for half an hour along the Corps front. The results obtained were that the enemy was discovered to be holding his front line, and five machine-guns were located. On this occasion, after the barrage ceased the figures were left standing to show the enemy that he had been fooled, with the idea that on the day of the real attack he would look twice before calling on his artillery to put down a barrage.

Plate XIVa illustrates the use of similar figures in connection with an operation of some magnitude on the Messines front on the 19th–20th September. This is of particular interest as the dummy figures were all made, erected and worked by a Field Company, R.E., a sample figure from the Camouflage Park being copied.

The plate shows the arrangement of the figures ; when the detonators were exploded they cut spunyarn which was holding the figures down.

The whole operation was a great success.

On the 26th September 280 figures were mounted and worked for some twenty minutes, during which time they were all smashed and rendered useless by machine-gun, rifle, and shell-fire. They were of material assistance to the attack of one infantry brigade, as they occupied the attention and drew the fire of the enemy from a direction in which flanking fire could have been brought to bear on the attack. The enemy reported on this occasion as follows :—

" The attack opened with drum-fire, with unheard-of intensity—behind a wall of dust and smoke the English infantry pressed forward between Langemarck and Hollebeke ; the enemy, attacking many times both sides of Langemarck, was continually beaten back by our fire."

On the greater part of this front no infantry attack other than silhouettes took place, so that the enemy's report testifies to the success of the ruse.

A very successful raid on the Hulluch front was carried out under cover of two dummy demonstrations.

The figures for the southern dummy raid were laid out in two rows of 60 figures each between the front and support trenches, and occupied a frontage of about 200 yards. The figures were raised into position at zero minus 40 minutes, and brought down a heavy barrage one minute later, which continued for three-quarters of an hour.

For the northern dummy raid another 120 figures were laid out between the front and support lines ; they were raised into position at zero minus three minutes behind a smoke barrage, and although this front was trench-mortared steadily from zero minus 30 minutes onwards, the figures were not noticed until zero plus one minute, when the hostile fire from trench-mortars and guns increased and lasted three-quarters of an hour. The trenches in rear of this dummy front and communication trenches in the vicinity were also heavily shelled. There were 116 hits on the southern group of figures, and 113 hits on the northern group.

The hostile barrage on the front of the real raid did not open until half an hour after zero.

In the case of another raid the figures were arranged in groups of seven, with three types of figure in each group, the centre one in each case being standing. There were four groups on either flank of the attack, placed in No-Man's-Land, the groups roughly arranged in echelon. The figures were raised by wire cables from pits about 200 yards away, each pit being manned by two men. The number of hits on these figures proved that they drew a large amount of fire, and their success was confirmed by the German wireless reports, which spoke of a raid on a 1,500 metre front, whereas the actual front was barely 400 yards.

25. MISCELLANEOUS PRODUCTS.

Dummy Heads.—These were first made by the French in winter, 1915, at Amiens, and were principally used by British snipers. Sniping was much more prevalent on the British front than on the French, and the value of these heads for the location of an enemy sniper was quickly recognized by certain sniping officers; thus they became a regular production of the factory.

Sniping died down very much in 1917, and the manufacture was discontinued.

Their success depended entirely on the way in which they were employed, which, needless to say, in turn depended entirely on the training and keenness of the individuals using them.

Certain sniping officers who used them intelligently were enabled to put an absolute stop to sniping on their front, so rapid and accurate was their location of the enemy snipers.

Plate XV shows one method of using dummy heads for locating snipers.

Sniping Suits.—These, as taken over from the French, consisted of loose-hooded blouses reaching to the knees, painted to harmonize with various backgrounds. Gloves and rifle covers were also provided.

Later, at the request of the Second Army Sniping School, a species of loose-fitting boiler suit was substituted, for the reason that the blouse was unsuitable for crawling. At the same time, the Symien pattern of sniping suit was produced—users could have their choice.

A large number of suits were made and issued, and were in great demand among units who were active in daylight patrols and sniping, particularly on the Third Army front after the enemy withdrawal in the spring of 1917.

Dummy Tanks.—These were still in the experimental stage at the end of the War.

Silhouette Practice Targets.—Head and shoulder targets were made and supplied to infantry and sniping schools to encourage marksmanship.

Similarly, special figure targets were made for training R.A.F. pilots in shooting on troops marching along a road. These were demanded and supplied only towards the last phase of the War.

26. CONCEALMENT OF POSITIONS.

This constituted the vast majority of the work of the Park, and the compliance with demands threw the greatest strain on its resources.

The principle that nature could be imitated by painted canvas was accepted from the French, and though suspicions were very soon aroused that this was not correct, it was not definitely disproved until the spring and summer of 1917, when an Experimental Section was established on the aerodrome at St. Omer, to whom every facility for flying and photography was given by the R.A.F.

Fortunately the demands for concealing positions were not very great or important during 1916. Considerable material was prepared for the Messines offensive, originally planned for autumn, 1916, but the offensive was postponed.

Meanwhile it had been found that the use of some substitute for grass, tied into wire or fish netting, gave better results than

I

grass itself. This idea was pursued, though it did not eventually oust painted canvas altogether till the spring of 1917, as preliminary difficulties of production and supply of netting had to be overcome. Raffia (or gardeners' bast) had been used by the French in their O.P. work for imitating grass, and this was the material adopted at first. Later canvas strips were used.

The Arras offensive in April, 1917, was furnished with both painted canvas and raffia netting. This was the first experience of a big and insistent demand, and though complete details of the proposed concentration, for which the amount of material required was worked out, were given in January, 1917, the actual amount required and furnished was more than double.

During 1917, a year of offensive, demands were made for the concealment of works of all kinds, *i.e.*, spoil from tunnelling, machine-gun positions, gas projectors, dumps, tanks, aeroplane hangars. These will be dealt with separately.

As an instance of the amount of camouflage used in one operation, the Cambrai offensive of 20.11.17 is instructive.

Three weeks' warning was received. Supplies were sent both from Wimereux and the Northern Special Works Park at Aire, to supplement those from Amiens. Additional officers and all available transport were also sent to assist. About 450,000 square yards of wire-netting and fish-netting camouflage, and painted scrim were supplied. In addition, special nets were made at Wimereux for 400 tanks, equivalent in area to about 40,000 square yards, making a grand total of nearly 500,000 sq. yds.

For the first time concealment was provided for concentration of the troops themselves, existing cover in villages and woods being supplemented, and a camp completely covered by a comprehensive horizontal cover over the whole area of bivouacs.

This offensive is also unique for the reason that fair warning was received, and comparative quiet on the rest of the front enabled all available resources for camouflage to be concentrated.

Generally speaking, every Corps camouflage officer was fairly well supplied with air photographs of gun positions in his area. Great difficulty was, however, experienced in getting photographs taken quickly of *particular* positions, which was an essential precaution. The only solution of this difficulty would seem to be the definite attachment of a photographic machine to the Camouflage Service in each Army.

In February, 1918, the principle was established of having mosaic air maps made of each Corps front at regular periods, whereby gun positions might be constantly examined, or batteries sited with reference to facilities for concealment. This was, perhaps, the greatest step towards scientific camouflage made during the War. The offensive of March, 1918, and the subsequent course of operations brought it to a premature end.

27. GUN POSITIONS.

It has been already stated that canvas sewn up into large rectangular sheets, painted to give a true representation of the locality, was used at first. The sizes of sheets varied according to the type of gun and position. 36 ft. × 36 ft. was selected as a standard size for an 18-pdr. The canvas used was obtained from Ordnance in bales 6 ft. wide. It is at once obvious that a very large amount of sewing was involved. At first this was done by man power, but very shortly motor-driven sewing-machines, operated by women, were installed.

The covers were erected over the gun on some sort of frame-work and came down to the ground on all sides, the whole forming a mound. This mound system obtained until the autumn of 1917, when it was condemned in a general sense by the result of experiments at St. Omer, and was replaced by the "flat top." This was adopted also by the French, who were impressed by the experiments. The value of canvas in the form of painted sheets was definitely discredited by this time also, as it was found that canvas, having no texture (i.e., containing no shadow) "blazed" photographically when the sun was anywhere except directly overhead.

In August, 1916, a portable set for 18-pdrs. was evolved, consisting of a 30 ft. × 30 ft. fish-net, garnished with dyed raffia, and a light iron frame of arches supported on four gas-pipe uprights with appropriate guys (see Plates XVI and XVII). This was issued for trial and report to several batteries and so favourably reported on that it became a standard article of manufacture.

In the various offensives of 1917 every 18-pdr. taking part was equipped with a portable set. As the supply of iron fell short, a wooden set was substituted.

Sets for heavier guns were also issued later, but, not being a success, were soon abandoned.

Further experience with these sets brought to light two very serious defects :—

(i) The fading of the green dye in strong sunlight.
(ii) The inflammability of the net and raffia.

(i) This was solved by abandoning the use of raffia and substituting canvas strips, painted with water-paint. A threatened shortage of raffia (which came from Mozambique) precipitated this decision. Special machines were evolved for painting and stripping canvas in large quantities, which effected a great saving in expense, and led to enormously increased production.

It may be mentioned that a satisfactory green dye was never found, even by the enemy, as evidenced by examination of his camouflage materials. The French dyed their materials up to the last, but the result was not really good.

(ii) So alarmed were the gunners at the number of fires that occurred, that in some cases the use of unfireproofed camouflage was forbidden.

The problem was attacked in two ways :—

(a) By attempts at fireproofing, and
(b) By endeavouring to fix the nets well out of reach of the flash of discharge.

(a) Fireproofing was never satisfactorily solved until the summer of 1918. The problem was submitted to England in autumn, 1916, but no satisfactory solution was forthcoming.

Apparently no chemical was known which rendered material fireproof and yet was itself waterproof. The only salt found that did fulfil these conditions was APM (magnesium ammonium phosphate) ; this was hurriedly adopted and ordered, only to show that it was unstable in practice and, further, seemed to cause the decomposition of the glue, paint and nets, so it was abandoned.

Meanwhile experiments were being made by a new process to fireproof the material (canvas) itself. This was eventually successful, but the termination of hostilities coincided with the placing of orders.

It should be mentioned that the French were equally baffled by the problem.

(b) The second method was more successful, so much so that in 1918 the question of fireproofing was re-submitted to the R.A., and the answer was that no trouble had been experienced, and that therefore it was only necessary in isolated cases.

The panic of 1917 was largely due to the massing of enormous numbers of guns in very confined areas, the incessant shooting, and the destructive effect of area shoots by the enemy.

Portable sets were issued up to the autumn of 1917, but the advent of the " flat top " killed them, as a set which could be erected horizontally over the gun ceased to be portable. In the end, guns simply carried a net without supports.

The later trend of experiments was in the direction of a frame that could be fastened to some portion of the gun, and support a net covering an area on either side of the gun.

It is impossible to particularize on the treatment of heavy guns. Sufficient material was issued (wire- or fish-netting indiscriminately), depending on the supply of wire- or fish-netting at the time. In many cases a definite disguise was adopted, such as a house, haystack, railway truck.

The most difficult problem that arose, perhaps, was that of snow camouflage. In 1916 practically nothing was done. Snow fell early in the winter of 1917, before the middle of December, and lasted some three or four weeks. White calico, obtained from Ordnance, was issued. It was intended to issue it in the form of large irregular patches, but the enormous amount of sewing involved and the eventual suddenness of the demand prevented this; consequently it was distributed, partly in rolls and partly in large irregular patches, which were placed on top of the existing nets, and to cover the blast marks.

In places where the snow did not present an unbroken surface these patches were of value; but where the whole countryside was completely covered, nothing was of any avail, and the aeroplane reigned supreme.

28. Concealment of Spoil.

Large quantities of painted scrim were issued for this purpose to Tunnelling and Field Companies. Scrim, being of a very much more open mesh than canvas, and therefore possessing texture, proved suitable for this purpose, when properly applied.

This was chiefly supplied during and after the summer of 1917.

29. Machine-Gun Positions.

Dealings with Machine-Gun Companies were never as extensive as they might have been. A sporadic demand was met by the design of the "pop-up" cover (*Plate* XVIII). This was extensively employed on the defence line work in the winter of 1917–18.

In July, 1918, at the request of the Inspector of M.G. Units, G.H.Q., a portable cover was designed to be carried by every gun.

After various trials, a scrim cover, 8 ft. × 8 ft., furnished with odd bunches of raffia, and painted grass-colour one side and earth the other, was adopted and issued during September and October, 1918. A label was attached to every cover with the following simple instructions as to general principles of concealment :—

How to Use this Camouflage—It is only meant for Open Warfare.

1. There is no magic in this cover. You *must* use local material, such as grass, weeds, twigs, earth, rubbish, as the case may be, or else you'll be SPOTTED easily.

2. Choose a DARK BACKGROUND and NEVER get on a SKYLINE. Shadows help to conceal you from enemy aircraft.

3. Use the GREEN side when on grass or vegetation, the BROWN side on earth or rubbish.

4. When in position, DON'T MOVE unless you have to; then move gradually.

5. Wrap a piece of canvas or puttee round barrel to stop reflection. Look to your condenser and fittings.

6. DON'T select a position near any conspicuous landmark. Keep an eye open for alternative positions.

7. Your face shows up a long way ; wear a mask.

No information was received as to the usefulness of this cover, and it is doubtful whether it had much practical trial owing to the rapid advance at that time.

30. MISCELLANEOUS WORKS.

Projector Emplacements.—The extensive use of gas-projectors instead of cylinders initiated dealings with the Special Brigade. A small illustrated pamphlet was got out and issued to every unit, setting forth the principles of camouflage as far as they were concerned (*see Plates* XIX, XX and XXI).

In January, 1918, an officer was attached to the Special Brigade for the purpose of lecturing and demonstrating to every unit. This had very good results.

Painted scrim was chiefly used, sometimes being reinforced by tufts of painted grass or raffia.

Dumps.—Many requests were made for the camouflaging of large depôts, such as Abancourt and Audruicq. Such an undertaking was manifestly impossible ; similarly in the case of more advanced dumps. It was always pointed out that camouflage of ammunition dumps in forward areas was only possible if the site were deliberately chosen with an eye to concealment, and if due notice were given, so that the camouflage could be erected before the dump was constructed. This was hardly ever done.

One or two dumps were, however, concealed—it is believed successfully—notably one near Hill Top, north of Ypres, in October, 1917. This dump was about 400 yds. long by 24 ft. wide, situated between a road and a railway. It was converted into a camouflaged roof tunnel, averaging 10 ft. high, of a variegated assortment of colours. The tumbled and broken nature of the ground all round assisted greatly. It was about 400 yds. behind the old front line of 1916–17.

Tanks.—In January, 1917, an officer was attached permanently to the Tank Corps, to act as their adviser.

All the materials they required for the early offensive in 1917 were supplied by the Park until they were able to organize their own manufacture and supply, after which they were self-supporting, except for occasional or sudden big demands, such as that for the Cambrai offensive.

Camps and Trains.—The concealment of camps was only attempted during the summer of 1918, when many headquarters were situated in the midst of the devastated area and would have been very conspicuous to night bombers.

The most comprehensive work was done for the Fourth Army H.Q. near Peronne. The result was said to be very inconspicuous to the eye of an observer, and was undoubtedly so at night. Photographically it was fairly obvious. 80,000 sq. yds. of material were used.

Several other H.Q.s were also done, including the trains of both Third and Fourth Army Commanders.

Hangars.—In August, 1917, the R.A.F. asked for a supply of painted covers for their Bessonneau hangars in order to make them less conspicuous at night. A few experimental covers were made, and having been favourably reported on, the manufacture was continued.

These covers were very large, each consisting of four pieces of scrim 50 ft. × 42 ft. each, hemmed all round, eyeletted at 3 ft. intervals, and painted.

The amount of sewing entailed was enormous, and kept all sewing machines going night and day for a considerable time during the first urgency of the order. Wimereux was the only park that was able to tackle the order.

This difficulty was represented to the R.A.F. with the suggestion that the covers should be supplied from England. This was agreed to, but the covers did not begin to arrive until October, 1918.

In all, 845 covers were supplied, equivalent to 800,000 sq. yds. of scrim.

Road Screening.—Though this was at first declared to be outside the sphere of camouflage, it was eventually undertaken in August, 1917, in order to standardize types and to relieve Armies and Corps of the trouble of starting factories of their own, the Park having already the necessary experience and facilities for the work.

The heaviest demand for road screening occurred as a result of the German capture of Kemmel in April, 1918. So urgent was the consequent demand that the factory at Wormhoudt concentrated all its personnel on this alone. In five weeks 163,000 sq. yds. of road screening was made and issued from this factory. This was equivalent to $1\frac{1}{2}$ miles of screening, 6 ft. high, per day.

31. WORK OF EXPERIMENTAL SECTION.

This section, which has already been alluded to, was formed in May, 1917, principally by Northern Special Works Park, and was located on the flying ground at St. Omer. It consisted of one officer and eight other ranks. Later it was joined by another officer. It was closed down in November, 1917, when the weather became too unsettled for further investigation.

Subjects for experiments were forwarded to this section through the three parks, copies of the results of observations, comments and photographs were sent to each park for circulation.

Every camouflage officer paid visits, and the majority flew over the exhibits.

It was also visited by the French and Americans.

Apart from valuable information on the subject of colour values, shadows, materials, photographic appearance of various terrain, etc., etc., it may be said that the principal results of these experiments were :—

(*a*) The flat top principle.
(*b*) The deliberate creation of irregular shadows by incorporating irregular masses of opaque material in all wire- or fish-netting camouflage.
(*c*) Mosaic photographs of Corps areas.

At the end of the War a great deal of research work still remained to be done, the science of camouflage being still in its infancy.

In July, 1918, the Experimental Section was reconstructed at Wimereux, as provided for in the reorganization which was eventually authorized in October, 1918.

Results of experiments carried out at Wimereux, and also selected examples of work at the front, were issued to each Army camouflage officer and factory.

A monthly conference was held at the office of the Controller which was attended by the Army camouflage officers, the O.C. Base factories, the experimental and chemist officers.

At these conferences questions of policy, both as regards work in the field and work in the factories, were decided. The results of any experiments or experiences were communicated also.

32. ENEMY CAMOUFLAGE.

From numerous captured documents it appears that the results achieved in our Army by the use of camouflage were so successful that the enemy was impressed by its necessity, and great efforts were made to promote scientific camouflage in the German Army both by appealing to common sense and by disciplinary methods. Many of the documents furnish testimony to the particular success achieved by British batteries. It would have been interesting to learn his views on other branches of camouflage, such as O.P.s and Chinese attacks, but apparently nothing was captured referring to these.

Large quantities of enemy camouflage materials were eventually captured in the summer of 1918. From these it was evident that he was a long way behind us in the manufacture of artificial camouflage, whilst there were no grounds for supposing that he displayed any better aptitude for concealment than our own.

The following notes on enemy methods were circulated in February, 1918. Nothing of importance to add to this was subsequently found, beyond the adoption of artificial material :—

Summary of Information, 20.2.18.

Preliminary Concealment.

As a general rule preliminary concealment has been neglected, with the result that subsequent concealment, though well carried out, has been of small value. There are signs, however, that the enemy is beginning to pay more attention to this subject.

The material used is for the most part obtained locally, in the shape of reeds, grass, branches, yew, ivy, etc.

Concealment of Completed Works.

Considerable care is taken to conceal completed works. Turfing is a favourite method, and the slopes are made gentle. In the Dunes, concrete has been given a rough and wrinkled surface to make it resemble the natural surface.

Frequently batteries are placed in trenches. Natural cover, such as afforded by ruins, wood, etc., is made use of wherever possible. In woods the existing cover is thickened by addition of branches concealing not only the emplacement but also tracks and shelters. It has been observed in a few instances that a lane has been cut through the intervening branches to allow shells to pass. This, of course, is not visible in a vertical photograph.

Tracks.

Considerable attention is evidently paid to the concealment of tracks—either by (a) digging trenches and then covering them over, (b) utilizing and supplementing existing cover of hedges and woods, (c) leading tracks past a position to a road or dummy position. But these precautions are frequently neglected in the preliminary stages.

Attention is also paid to track discipline, and the confining of traffic to one track.

Blast Marks.—These are carefully concealed, but the actual method employed is not known. The enemy frequently runs his guns into their emplacements by a ramp in front, which is subsequently covered by an embrasure screen. It is possible that this ramp takes a good deal of the blast and throws the rest upwards.

Flash Screens.—Artificial screens are used, but without conspicuous success. Smoke is also employed, but it is often possible to see flashes through it.

Dummy Flashes and Shell Bursts.—It is known that dummy flashes and shell bursts are adopted. They are employed in conjunction with dummy positions, or some distance away from the real positions.

Road Screens.—Methods of road screening are similar to our own.

O.P.s and Snipers' Posts.—Gauze is occasionally used to conceal loopholes of O.P.s and Snipers' Posts; but for the most part the enemy relies on the solid protection afforded by concrete and merely makes the loophole of irregular shape. He does not appear to recognize the fact that O.P.s are often given away by tracks leading up to them.

Observation from the branches of tall trees is very common.

Snipers and patrols use camouflaged suits; dummy heads and other devices for drawing fire have been employed occasionally.

Wire.—Wire entanglements have recently been made of fine barbed wire arranged in fences so that it is only visible on an aeroplane photograph when conditions of photography are very favourable.

Obliteration of Ranging.—The enemy occasionally fills up shell-holes to defeat photographic record of counter-battery work, and has fired flashes to imitate our shell bursts, to defeat aeroplane observation.

Table I.

SPECIAL WORKS PARK.

WAR ESTABLISHMENT (MARCH, 1916).

(i) *Personnel.*

Detail.	Personnel.					Bicycles.	Motor Cars.
	Officers.	Warrant Officers.	Staff Serjts. and Serjts.	Rank and File.	Total.		
Major	1				1		3
Captain	1				1		
Subalterns	4(a)				4		
Quartermaster ...	1				1		
Company-Serjt.-Major		1			1		
C.Q.M.S.			1		1		
Clerks			1	1	2		
Serjeants			2		2		
Corporals				3	3		
2nd Corporals ...				3	3		
Sappers				60	60(b)		
Pioneers				10	10(d)		
Total (excl. Attached)	7	1	4	77	89		3
Attached :							
Officers	3(c)				3		
R.A.M.C. ...				1	1		
Drivers, A.S.C., M.T.				6	6		
Batmen				10	10		
Total (incl. Attached)	10	1	4	94	109		3

(a) Includes 1 Mechanical Engineer.   (b) Includes 6 Lance-Corporals.
c) Artists.   (d) Includes 1 Lance-Corporal.

(ii) *Transport.*

Detail.	Motor Cars.	30-cwt. Lorry.	Box Cars. 15-cwt.	Drivers.
For Personnel	3	–	–	3
For Delivery	–	1	1	3
Total	3	1	1	6

S.D.2.

10th May, 1916.

Table II.
HEADQUARTERS, CAMOUFLAGE SERVICE.
War Establishment.

Detail.	Officers.	Warrant Officers.	Staff Serjts. and Serjts.	Corporals.	Rank and File.	Total.	Motor Cars.	Box Cars.	Motor Cycles.
Controller of Camouflage ...	1(a)					1	1	1	1
Assistant Controller of Camouflage (Major)	1					1			
Experimental and *Liaison* Officer (Captain, R.E.)	1					1			
Chemist (Captain, R.E.)	1(b)					1			
Stores Officer and Statistics (Subaltern) ...	1					1			
Clerks		1(c)	1	1		3			
Draughtsman ...					1	1			
Chemist's Assistants					1(d)	1			
Attached:									
Batmen (Scale B)					3	3			
Drivers, A.S.C., M.T.					2	2			
Total (excl. Attd.)	5	1	1	1	2	10	1	1	1
Total (incl. Attd.)	5	1	1	1	7	15	1	1	1

CAMOUFLAGE SERVICE AT ARMY H.Q.

Detail.	Officers.	Warrant Officers.	Staff Serjts. and Serjts.	Corporals.	Rank and File.	Total.	Motor Cars.	Box Cars.	Motor Cycles.
Army Camouflage Officer (Major)	1					1	1		
Clerk			1			1	1		
Draughtsman ...					1	1			
Total (excl. Attd.)	1		1		1	3	1		
Attached:									
Batman (Scale B)					1	1			
Driver, A.S.C., M.T. ...					1	1			
Total (incl. Attd.)...	1		1		3	5	1		

(a) Lieut.-Colonel, Class X. (b) or Captain seconded to R.E. (c) Class 1. (d) Sapper.

Table IIa.

CAMOUFLAGE SERVICE AT CORPS H.Q.

War Establishment.

Detail.	Offrs.	Corpls.	R. & F.	Total.
Corps Camouflage Officer (Captain)	1			1
Assistant Corps Camouflage Officer (Subaltern) ...	1			1
Clerk		1		1
Total (excl. Attached) ...	2	1		3
Attached:				
Batman (Scale B) ...			1	1
From Army Factory ...			3 (a)	3 (a)
Total (incl. Attached) ...	2	1	1	4

(a) Includes 1 N.C.O.

ARMY CAMOUFLAGE FACTORY.

War Establishment.

Detail.	Offrs.	Sjts.	Cpls.	R. &F.	Ttl.	Motor Cycles.
Captain	1				1	
Subaltern	1				1	1 (a)
Clerk			1		1	
Serjeant		1			1	
Corporal			1		1	
2nd-Corporals				3	3	
Sappers				18 (b)	18	
Pioneers				2	2	
Total (excl. Attached) ...	2	1	2	23	28	1
Attached:						
Batman (Scale B) ...				1	1	
Total (incl. Attached) ...	2	1	2	24	29	1

(a) With side car.   (b) Includes 1 Lce.-Corpl.

ARMY CAMOUFLAGE FACTORY.

Distribution of N.C.O.s and Rank and File by Trade.

Artists	2
Blacksmith	1
Bricklayer or Mason	1
Carpenters and Joiners	5
Clerk	1
Fitter	1
Painters	7
Tinsmith or Plumber	1
Engine Driver or Boiler Attendant ...	1
Electrician	1
Miscellaneous	3
Pioneers	2
Total	26

Table IIb.

Base Camouflage Factory.

War Establishment.

Detail.	Officers.	Warrant Officers.	Staff Serjts. and Serjts.	Corporals.	Rank and File.	Q.M.A.A.C.	Total.	Motor Cars.	Bicycles.
Major	1						1	1	4
Captains	3						3		
Subalterns	6						6		
Coy. Serjt.-Major (W.O. Cl. II) ...		1					1		
Coy. Qrmr. Sertj.			1				1		
Clerks			1	1	2		4		
Serjeants			4				4		
Corporals				8			8		
2nd-Corporals ...					10		10		
Sappers					162 }	(a)	162		
Pioneers					20 }		20		
Total (excl. Attd.) ...	10	1	6	9	194		220	1	4
Attached :									
R.A.M.C.					1		1		
Sanitary details					2(b)		2		
Drivers,A.S.C.,M.T.					10		10		
Q.M.A.A.C. Personnel :									
Officials (Asst. Administrators)	5(c)						5		
Workers						25 (d)	25		
Total (incl. Attd.) ...	15	1	6	9	207	25	263	1	4

(*a*) Includes 14 Lce.-Corpls. (*b*) Category B. (*c*) 1 to supervise Q.M.A.A.C. personnel, 4 to supervise 400–600 French women. (*d*) Includes 2 typists. (Note.—Batmen provided on Scale C.)

(ii) *Transport.*

Detail.	Bicycles.	Motor Cars.	3-ton Lorries.	Ford Box Cars.	Drivers.
For personnel .	4	1	–	–	1
For delivery ...	–	–	3	3	9
Total	4	1	3	3	10

Table IIc.
COMPARATIVE TABLE.

	Offrs.	Asst. Admin. QMAAC	W.O.'s Cl. I.	W.O.'s Cl. II.	S.Sjts. and Sjts.	Rank and File	QMAAC	Total.	Bicycles.	Motor Cars.	Box Cars, 15 cwt.	Motor Cycles.	Lorries 3-ton	Lorries 30 cwt.
I. New Establishment:—														
Controller of														
Camouflage ...	3	—	1	—	1	8	—	15	—	1	1	1	—	—
5 Armies ...	5	—	—	—	5	15	—	25	—	5	—	—	—	—
16 Corps (a) ...	32	—	—	—	—	32	—	64	—	—	—	—	—	—
Base Factory ...	10	5	—	1	6	216	25	263	4	1	3(b)	—	3	—
4 Army Factories	8	—	—	—	4	104	—	116	—	1	—	4	—	—
Total ...	60	5	1	1	16	375	25	483	4	7	4	5	3	—
2. Old Establishment:—														
Special Works Park (Leaflet No. 1301) ...	58	1	—	1	12	383	—	455	4	6	4	4	—	3
Increase ...	2	4	1	—	4	—	25	28*	—	1	—	1	3	—
Decrease ...	—	—	—	—	—	8	—	—	—	—	—	—	—	3

(a) Excludes Cavalry, Australian and Canadian Corps. (b) Ford Box Cars.

* NOTE.—Of this total all are Q.M.A.A.C., plus Batmen on Scale "C" for Base Factory.

Photo i.

Photo ii.—Typical French Work.

CAMOUFLAGE SERVICE.

Photo iii.

Photo iv.—Typical French Work.

CAMOUFLAGE SERVICE.

Photo v.—Back View of O.P. Tree.

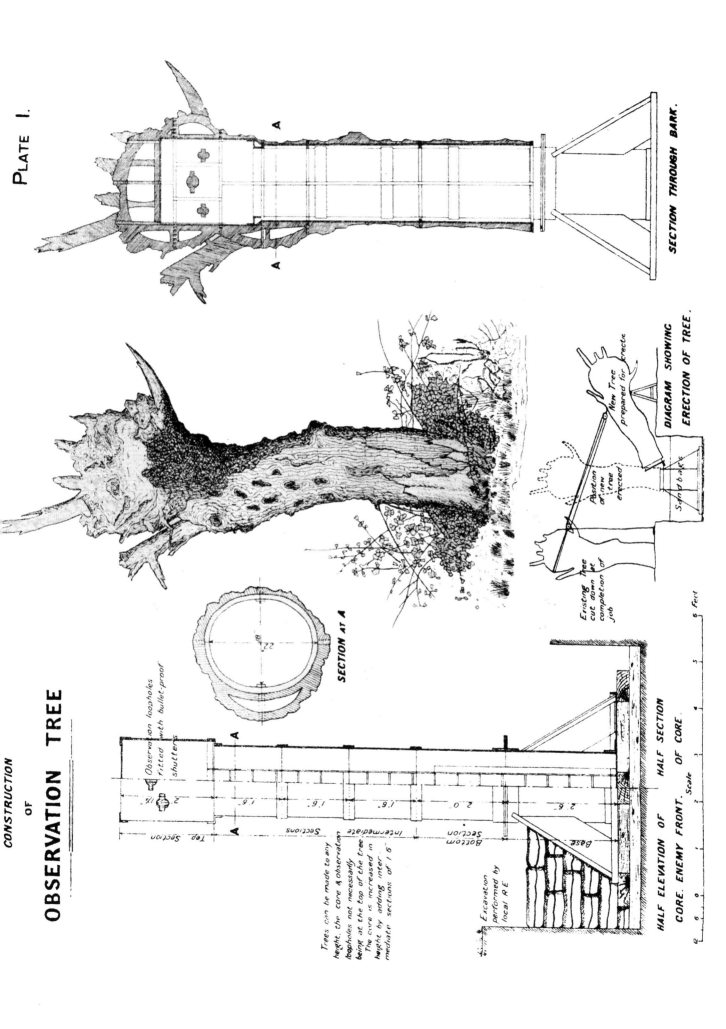

PLATE I.

CONSTRUCTION
OF
OBSERVATION TREE

SECTION THROUGH BARK.

SECTION AT A

DIAGRAM SHOWING ERECTION OF TREE.

Existing Tree cut down at completion of job

Position of new tree erected

New Tree prepared for erection

Sand bags

Observation loopholes fitted with bullet-proof shutters

Trees can be made to any height, the core & observation loopholes not necessarily being at the top of the tree.
The core is increased in height by adding intermediate sections of 1'6"

Top Section

Intermediate Sections

Bottom Section

Excavation performed by local R.E.

Base

HALF ELEVATION OF   HALF SECTION
CORE. ENEMY FRONT.   OF CORE.
Scale
2   0   3   6 Feet

PLATE II.

O.P. IN PLOEGSTEERT WOOD AT U-21.b.25.25.(Sheet 28)

Description.

A stump of oak to hold observer. 11 feet high.
2 Ft 2 Ins diameter. Approach through
PLOEGSTEERT Wood Trench railway near.
Ground broken and boggy About 20 feet
from Front Line trench It is proposed
to increase the height of the tree by 3 feet
as it is important to obtain good observation, and to increase the height of the parapet
accordingly; latter work to be done by occupants

View from S.E.

PLATE III.

Excavation for Tree at M.O.24

"German House" Bois de Ploegsteert

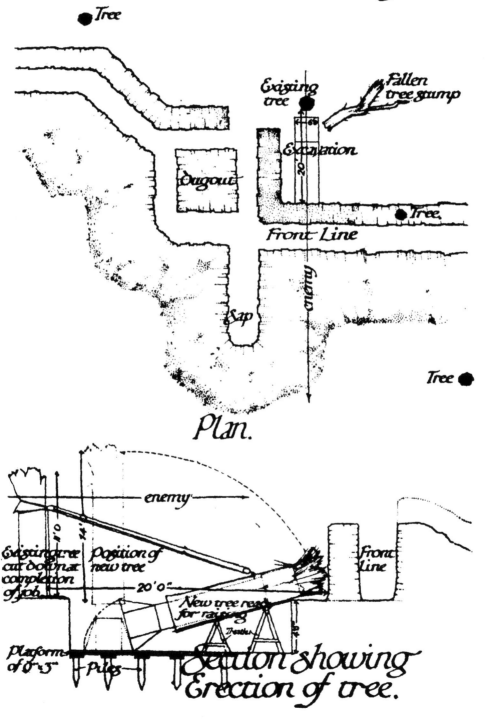

Plan.

Section showing Erection of tree.

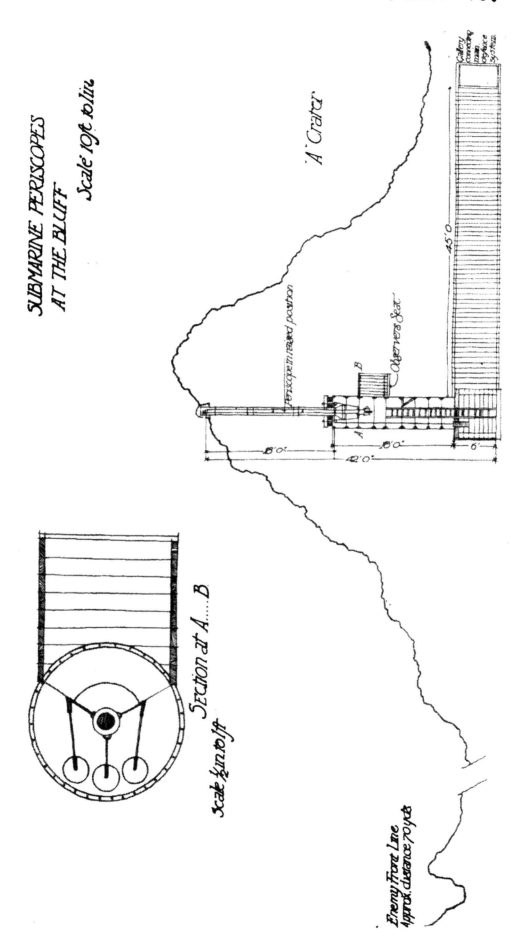

PLATE IV.

SUBMARINE PERISCOPES
AT THE BLUFF

Scale 10ft. to 1in.

'A' Crater

Periscope in raised position

Observer's Seat

Section at A....B

Scale ½in. to 1ft.

Enemy Front Line
Approx. distance 70 yds.

PLATE V.

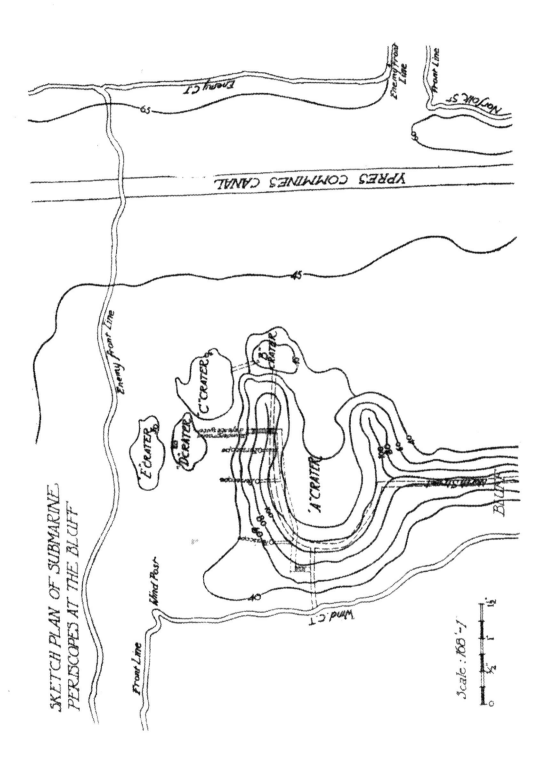

SKETCH PLAN OF SUBMARINE
PERISCOPES AT THE BLUFF

Scale : 168´=1´

PLATE VI.

Reconnaissance by L⁺ O.P. Bernard   Date 27.6.16.
Second Army   Canadian Corps   Heavy Artillery
Situation (S28) (34.611) near Lovers Lane

"CHOAT"

Description. Shattered Fir Tree. To be replaced by artificial tree stump
containing 7'6" periscope Central point of observation required S.W.O.P to be used
primarily by 31 Siege battery O.C Capt Donelly R.G.A Transport by Lorry to Wood-
cote House from there by tramway to Rennec, then by hand to situation
Some awkward branches to be knocked off original tree while camouflage
is prepared

PLATE VII.

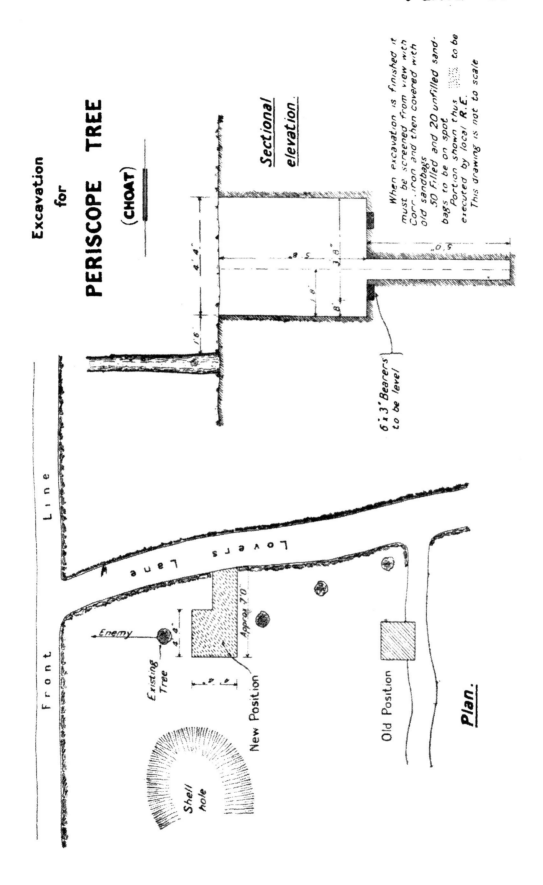

Excavation
for
PERISCOPE TREE
(CHOAT)

Sectional elevation.

When excavation is finished it
must be screened from view with
Corr. iron and then covered with
old sandbags
50 filled and 20 unfilled sandbags to be on spot
Portion shown thus ▨ to be
executed by local R.E.
This drawing is not to scale

6' x 3' Bearers
to be level

Front Line

Lovers Lane

Enemy

Existing Tree

New Position

Approx 70

Shell hole

Old Position

Plan.

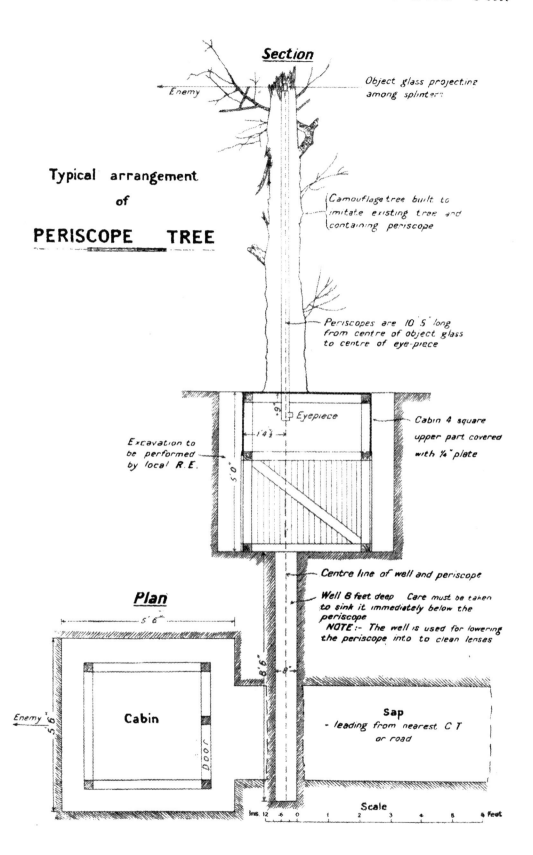

Plate VIII.

Typical arrangement of PERISCOPE TREE

Section

Plan

PLATE IX.

Excavation and fixing of trench O.P. - Type "OLIVER".

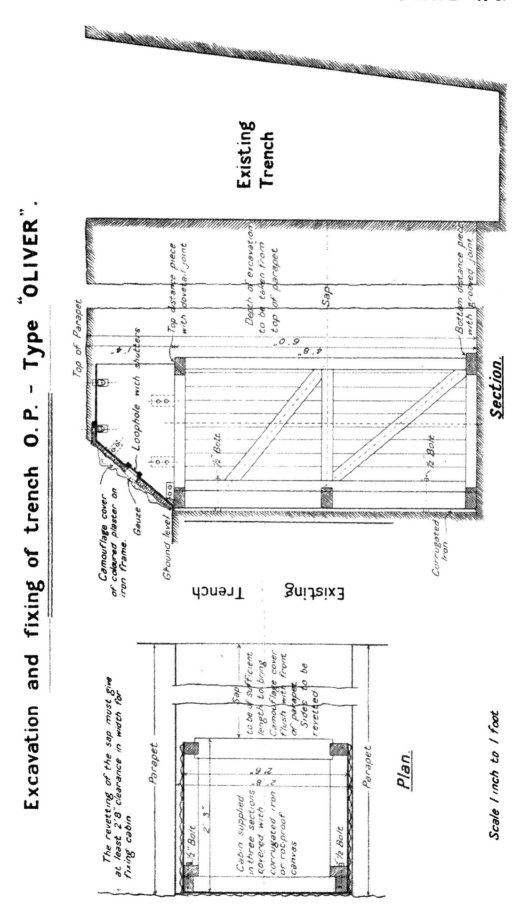

Section.

Existing Trench

Top of Parapet

Top distance piece with dovetail joint

Depth of excavation to be taken from top of parapet

Sap

Bottom distance piece with grooved joint

Loophole with shutters

Camouflage cover of coloured plaster on iron frame.

Gauze

Ground level

Corrugated Iron

½" Bolt

Existing Trench

Plan.

The revetting of the sap must give at least 2'8" clearance in width for fixing cabin.

Parapet

Sap to be of sufficient length to bring Camouflage cover flush with front of parapet. Sides to be revetted.

Cabin supplied in three sections covered with corrugated iron or rot-proof canvas

Parapet

½" Bolt

½" Bolt

Scale 1 inch to 1 foot

PLATE X.

Trench O. P. Type "ROLAND"

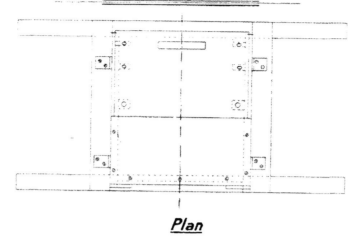

Plan

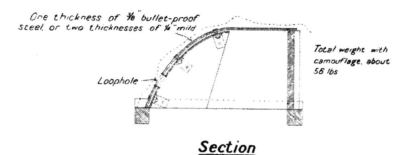

One thickness of ⅜" bullet-proof steel or two thicknesses of ¼" mild

Loophole

Total weight with camouflage, about 56 lbs

Section

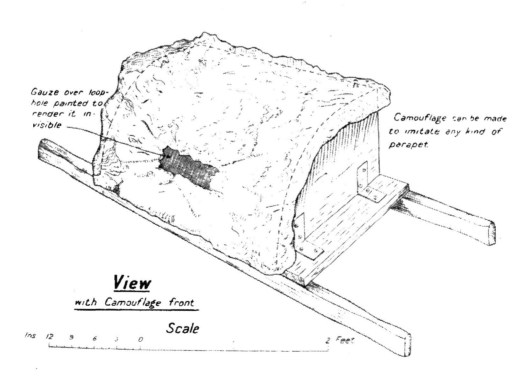

Gauze over loophole painted to render it invisible

Camouflage can be made to imitate any kind of parapet.

View
with Camouflage front

Scale

Ins 12 9 6 3 0   2 Feet

PLATE XI.

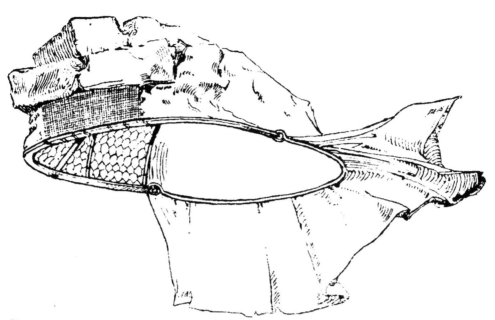

Portable Beehive O.P. unarmoured (weight about 10 lb.). Showing " brick " camouflage. Any surroundings can be similarly imitated.

Portable Beehive O.P. in use.

PLATE XII.

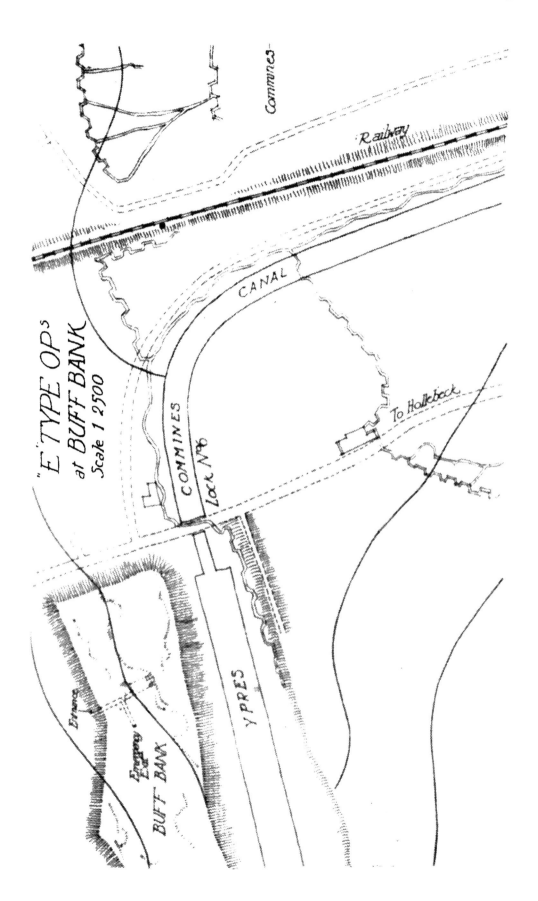

"E" TYPE OP^s
at BUFF BANK
Scale 1 2500

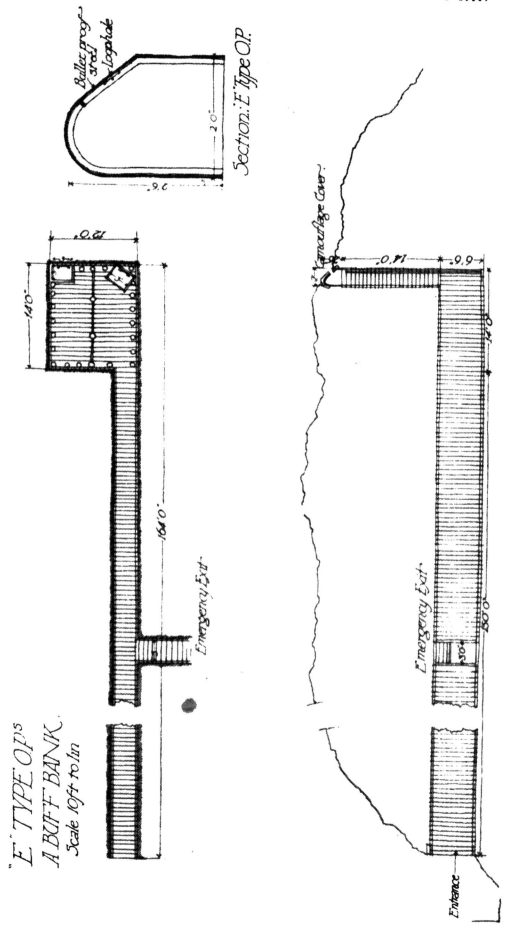

PLATE XIII.

PLATE XIV.

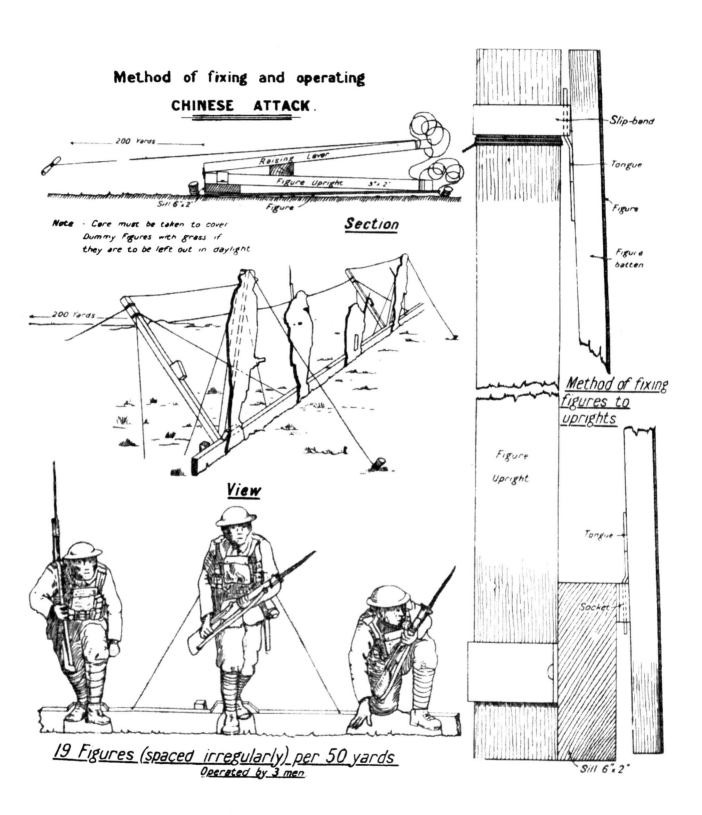

Method of fixing and operating
CHINESE ATTACK.

200 Yards

Raising Lever

Figure Upright 3". 2"

Sill 6"x 2"

Figure

Section

Note. Care must be taken to cover
Dummy Figures with grass if
they are to be left out in daylight

200 Yards

View

Slip-band

Tongue

Figure

Figure
batten

**Method of fixing
figures to
uprights**

Figure
Upright

Tongue

Socket

Sill 6"x 2"

19 Figures (spaced irregularly) per 50 yards
Operated by 3 men.

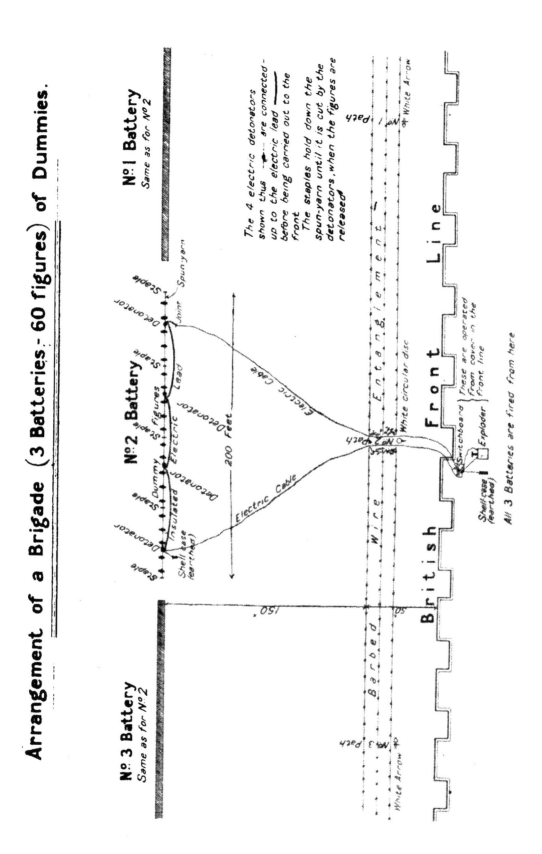

PLATE XIVA.

Arrangement of a Brigade (3 Batteries - 60 figures) of Dummies.

No. 1 Battery
Same as for No 2

No. 2 Battery

No. 3 Battery
Same as for No 2

The 4 electric detonators shown thus ⟶ are connected up to the electric lead ━━━ before being carried out to the front.

The staples hold down the spun-yarn until it is cut by the detonators, when the figures are released.

These are operated from cover in the front line

All 3 Batteries are fired from here

PLATE XV.

Method of locating enemy sniper by use of DUMMY HEADS.

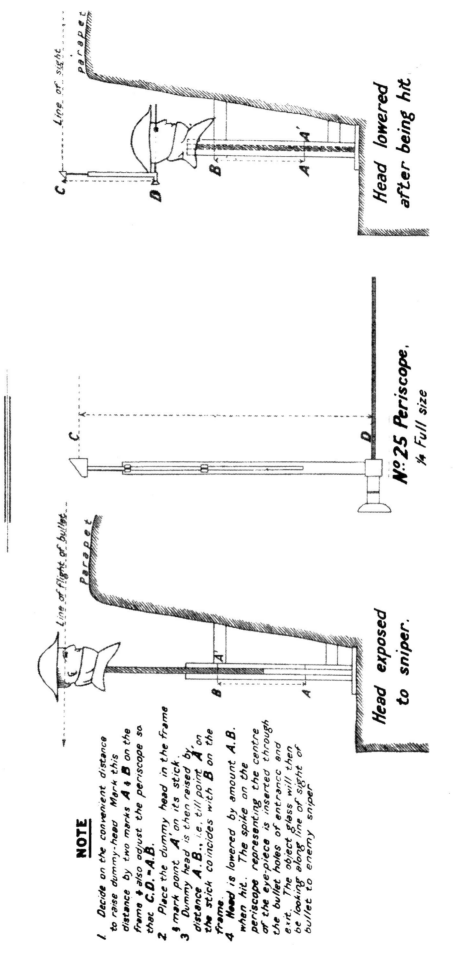

NOTE

1. Decide on the convenient distance to raise dummy-head Mark this distance by two marks **A** & **B** on the frame & also adjust the periscope so that **C.D.=A.B.**

2. Place the dummy head in the frame & mark point **A'** on its stick.

3. Dummy head is then raised by distance **A.B.**, i.e. till point **A'** on the stick coincides with **B** on the frame.

4. **Head** is lowered by amount **A.B.** when hit. The spike on the periscope representing the centre of the eye-piece is inserted through the bullet holes of entrance and exit. The object glass will then be looking along line of sight of bullet to enemy sniper.

Line of flight of bullet.

Parapet

B

A'

A'

Head exposed to sniper.

C

No. 25 Periscope, ¼ Full size

D

Line of sight

Parapet

C

D

B

A'

A'

Head lowered after being hit

PLATE XVI.

GUN FRAME and NET for 18 P.DR GUN & 4".5 HOW.R

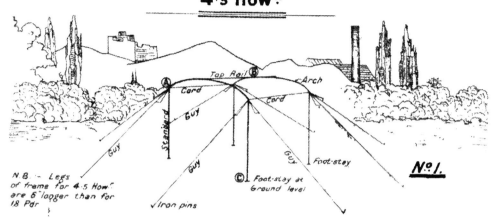

N.B. – Legs of frame for 4.5 How.R are 6" longer than for 18 Pdr

SKETCH SHOWING ARRANGEMENT OF FRAME AND GUYS.

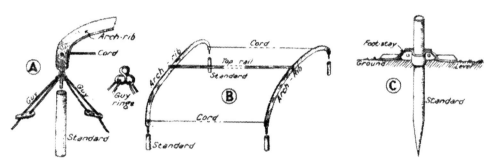

DETAIL SKETCHES

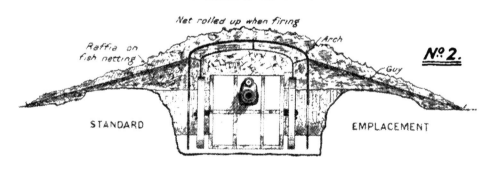

SKETCH OF GUN IN EMPLACEMENT

Notes on use –

1. Extend guys to full extent to get gentle slope
2. Roll up net completely on top of arch when firing to avoid danger of setting it alight
3. Best effect. Maximum cover is obtained by sinking both gun & frame as deep as possible
4. Quickest method of putting net over frame. Cut the cords & unroll net until it becomes a long sausage. Lay this sausage right over the middle of the arches like illustration N.º 2 then unroll the net towards the front and towards the back
5. Adapt colours to those of surroundings with mud

PLATE XVII.

GUN FRAME and NET for 18 P^{dr} GUN & 4$^{.''}$5 How^R.
Timber Pattern

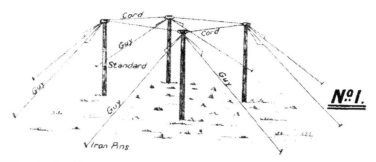

No. 1.

SKETCH SHOWING ARRANGEMENT OF FRAME AND GUYS.

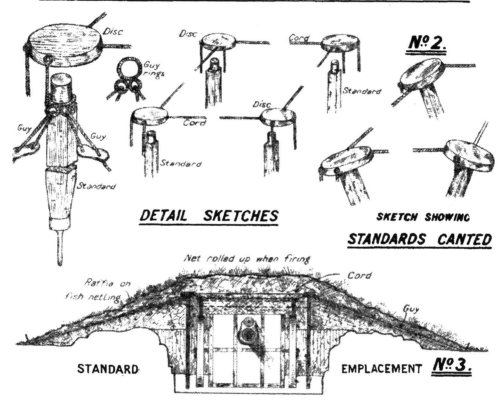

No. 2.

DETAIL SKETCHES

SKETCH SHOWING
STANDARDS CANTED

EMPLACEMENT No. 3.

SKETCH OF GUN IN EMPLACEMENT.

Notes on use -

1. Extend guys to full extent to get gentle slope
2. Roll up net completely on top of discs when firing to avoid danger of setting it alight
3. Best effect Maximum cover is obtained by sinking both gun and frame as deep as possible
4. Quickest method of putting net over frame Cut the cords & unroll net until it becomes a long sausage Lay this sausage right over the middle of the discs as in illustration No. 3 Then unroll the net towards the front and towards the back
5. Camouflage must be adapted to surroundings (a) in broken ground or bare earth, with mud. (b) if in grass by putting something dark on all excavated earth or light-coloured objects which would otherwise show through the net THIS IS ABSOLUTELY NECESSARY
6. Canted position (as Fig No. 2 & dotted lines in Fig. No. 3) can be used to alter profile and to lower height above ground level Alteration from vertical to canted position is made by altering length of end & side ropes which are provided extra long
7. Avoid regularity in shape

CAMOUFLAGE COVER
for
MACHINE GUN EMPLACEMENT.

Such a cover admits of firing being continued unobserved by a low-flying aeroplane overhead. When lowered it is practically flush with the ground

PLATE XVIII.

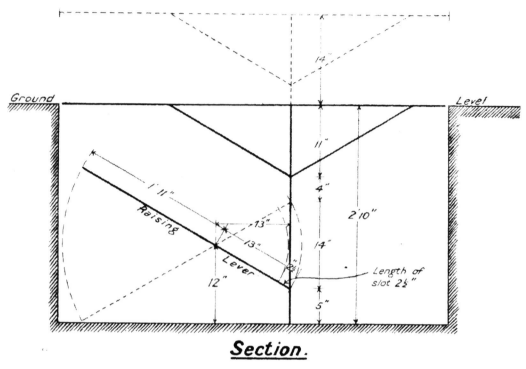

Section.

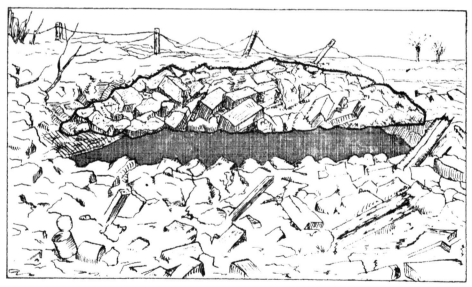

Raised position of a possible type of camouflage
cover made of painted canvas

PLATE XIX

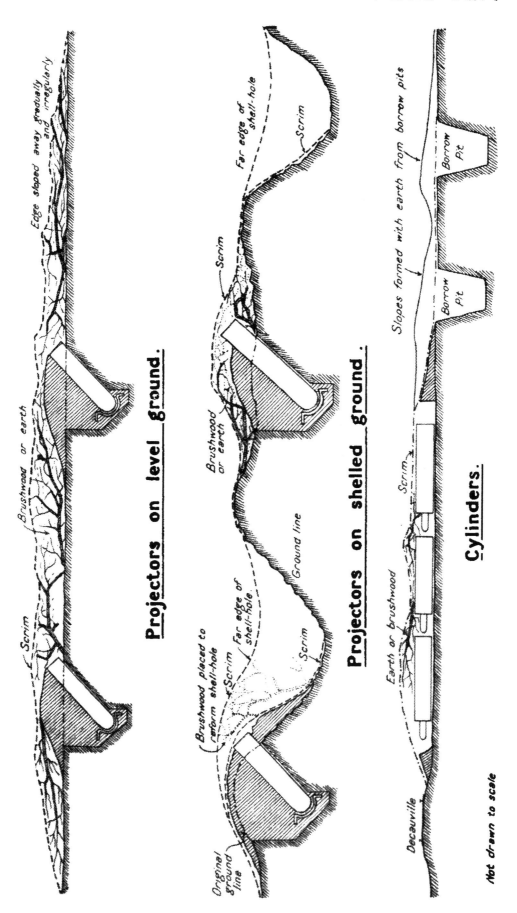

Projectors on level ground.

Edge sloped away gradually and irregularly

Brushwood or earth

Scrim

Projectors on shelled ground.

Far edge of shell-hole

Scrim

Scrim

Brushwood or earth

Brushwood placed to reform shell-hole

Scrim

Far edge of shell-hole

Scrim

Ground line

Original ground line

Cylinders.

Slopes formed with earth from borrow pits

Borrow Pit

Borrow Pit

Scrim

Earth or brushwood

Decauville

Not drawn to scale

PLATE XX.

IRREGULAR CAMOUFLAGE

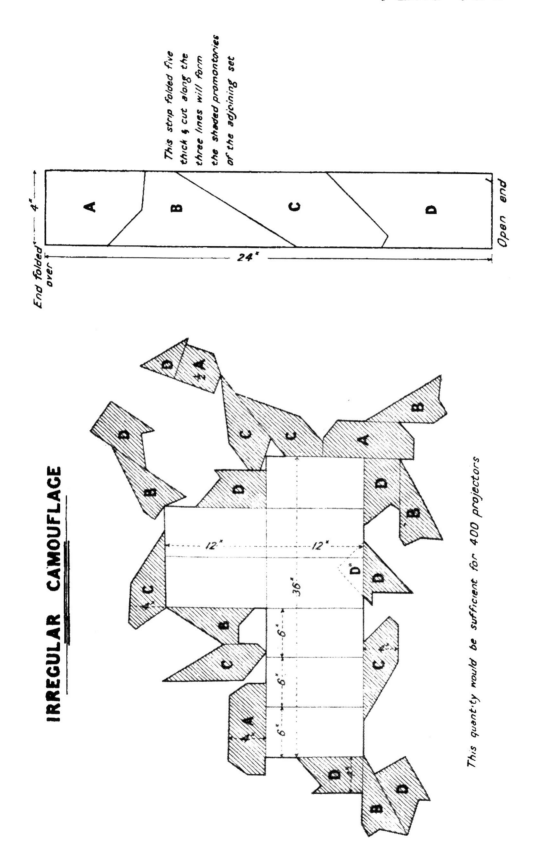

This strip folded five thick & cut along the three lines will form the shaded promontories of the adjoining set

End folded over

4"

24"

Open end

A

B

C

D

12"   12"

36"

6"   6"   6"   6"

This quantity would be sufficient for 400 projectors

PLATE XXI.

IRREGULAR CAMOUFLAGE

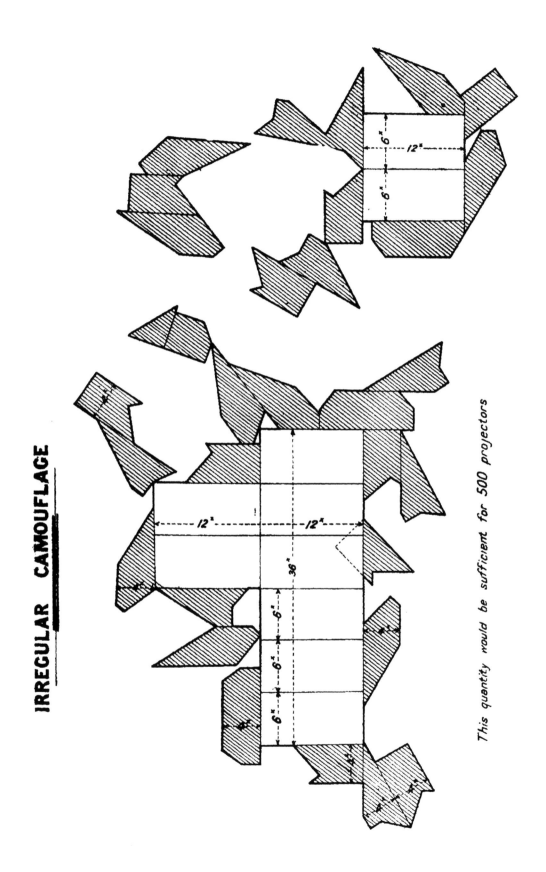

This quantity would be sufficient for 500 projectors

Table III.

FORM C 4.

..........................CAMOUFLAGE FACTORY.

	QUARTERLY FORECAST OF ORDNANCE STORES REQUIRED FOR ....QUARTER, 191			WEEKLY STOCK SHEET FOR SATURDAY, ...191		
	NOTE.—Cross out the heading which is not applicable.			These columns are only required to be completed for weekly stock sheets.		
Sect.	Item.	Unit.	Quantity required or stock in last Return.	Receipts	Issues.	Stock in hand.
2A	Eyelets, Brass E.	No.				
3	Wire, Iron S.W.G. No. 12	Lbs.				
	,, ,, ,, ,, 14	,,				
	,, ,, ,, ,, ...	,,				
7	Knives, Trimming	No.				
8A	Spun Yarn	Lbs.				
9A	Plaster of Paris	,,				
OIL PAINTS.	Green, Brunswick Dark ...	Cwts.				
	,, ,, Light ...	,,				
	Chrome, Lemon	,,				
	,, Mid.	,,				
	,, Orange	,,				
	Umber, Burnt	,,				
	,, Raw	,,				
	Sienna, Burnt	,,				
	,, Raw	,,				
	Red Oxide	,,				
	White Lead	,,				
	Yellow Ochre	,,				
	White Spirits	Galls.				
	Varnish, Japan Gold, Size ...	,,				
	Driers, Liquid Lead, Free ...	,,				
	Linseed Oil, Raw	,,				
DRY PAINTS.	Green, Brunswick Dark ...	Cwts.				
	,, ,, Light ...	,,				
	Chrome, Lemon	,,				
	,, Mid.	,,				
	,, Orange	,,				
	Umber, Burnt	,,				
	,, Raw	,,				
	Sienna, Burnt	,,				
	,, Raw	,,				
	Blue, Prussian	,,				
	,, Ultramarine	,,				
	Black	,,				
	Red Oxide	,,				
	Whitening	,,				
	Terra Alba	,,				
	Yellow Ochre	,,				
	A. P. M.	,,				
	Glue	,,				
	Linseed Oil, Boiled	Galls.				
	Varnish Copal	,,				
12	Sewing Machine Shuttles ...	No.				
13C	Thread, Linen Whited Brown :					
	No. 18	Reels				
	No. 25	,,				
	No. 50	,,				
	Calico	Sq. yds.				

K

Table IV.

FORM C 5.

....CAMOUFLAGE FACTORY.

MONTHLY INDENT FOR R.E. STORES REQUIRED FOR 191		WEEKLY STOCK SHEET FOR SATURDAY, ...191			
NOTE.—Cross out the heading which is not applicable.		These columns are only required to be completed for weekly stock sheets			
Item.	Unit.	Quantity required or stock in last Return.	Receipts	Issues.	Stock in hand.
Canvas, Hessian 72 ins.	yds. run				
„ Scrim 72 ins.	„ „				
Gauze Wire Tinned	ft. run				
Sapon	Tons				
Boiler Suits	No.				
Fish Nets	„				
Knives, Special Cross Cutting ...	Gross.				
PAINT BRUSHES.					
Long Handled, Large ...	„				
„ „ Medium ...	„				
„ „ Small ...	„				
ONE KNOT COPPER WIRE BOUND.					
No. 8	Doz.				
„ 6	„				
„ 4	„				
„ 2	„				
SASH TOOLS, LILY.					
No. 16	„				
„ 12	„				
„ 9	„				
„ 8	„				
„ 6	„				
„ 4	„				
FITCHES, HOG HAIR.					
No. 12	„				
„ 11	„				
„ 10	„				
„ 9	„				
„ 8	„				
„ 7	„				
„ 6	„				
„ 5	„				
„ 4	„				
Manganese Sulphate	Tons.				
Wire Netting	Rolls.				
Coir Lewing	„				
Corrugated Iron	Bundles				
Loophole Plates	No.				

Table V.

STATEMENT SHOWING GROSS EXPENDITURE OF CERTAIN STORES DURING THE WAR.

Description.	Quantity.	Remarks.
Oil, Linseed, Boiled ... Galls.	151,630	
,, ,, Raw ... ,,	7,065	
Glue ... ... Tons	435¼	
Canvas, Hessian 72 in. ... Yds.	10,561,500	
,, Scrim, 72 in. ... ,,	6,860,000	
Jean Khaki ... ... ,,	1,600,000	
Calico, White ... ... ,,	554,300	
Cotton ... ... Reels	28,660	
Sapon ... ... Tons	34¼	
Fish-nets (aver. 30 ft. x 30 ft.) No.	94,000	Nets varied in size ; total quantity is equivalent.
Wire Netting ... ... Rolls	142,645	
Paint, Dry ... ... Tons	3,022½	
,, G. in O. ... ... ,,	521¼	

Table VI.

DETAILED STATEMENT SHOWING TOTAL EXPENDITURE OF PAINTS DRY
AND GROUND IN OIL.

Colour.	Paint, Dry. Tons.	Paint, G. in O. Tons.
Brown Umber Turkey Burnt	302½	38¼
,, ,, Raw	61½	1
,, Terre de Sienna Burnt	43¼	15½
,, ,, ,, Raw	65	28¾
Yellow Chrome Lemon	290	45¾
,, ,, Mid Tint	119¾	19¼
,, ,, Orange	28½	6¾
Yellow Ochre	419¾	61
Vermilion	1¾	½
Lead White	1	105¼
Blue Ultramarine	14¾	2½
,, Prussian	15½	2¼
Green Brunswick Light	1,105½	123¾
,, ,, Dark	580½	16½
,, Emerald	2¾	8½
Black	45½	33¼
Whitening	325½	—
Red Venetian	12¾	3½
,, Oxide	12¾	6
Zinc Oxide	—	3
Total	3,448½	521¼

Table VII.

TOTAL OUTPUT OF CERTAIN CAMOUFLAGE MANUFACTURERS.

Concealment of Positions.

Painted Canvas Sheets. Sq. yds.	Wire Netting. Sq. yds.	Fish Netting. Sq. yds.	Portable Gun Sets.		Scrim. Sq. yds.	Road Screening. Sq. yds.
			18 pdr.	Heavy		
959,092	6,281,455	7,493,856	12,816	3,228	4,195,994	850,795

O.P.s and Miscellaneous.

O.P.s.			Portable O.P.s.		Snipers' Suits.	Dummy Heads.	Chinese Attack Figures.
Para-pet.	Tree.	Peri-scope	Armoured.	Un-armoured.			
581	45	92	920	1,706	4,795	2,741	12,553

Table VIII.

CAMOUFLAGE MATERIALS USED DURING THE ARRAS, MESSINES AND YPRES OFFENSIVES, 1917.

| Dates. | Period-Offensive. | Painted. | | Garnished Netting. | | Road Screening. Sq. yds. | Portable Gun Frames. Field. | Remarks. |
		Canvas Sheets. Sq. yds.	Scrim. Sq. yds.	Wire. Sq. yds.	Fish. Sq. yds.			
1.1.17 to 14.4.17, used by First and Third Armies	3½ months Arras	205,501	39,300	321,257	80,169	*Nil.*	379	
14.4.17 to 9.6.17, used by Second Army	8 weeks, Messines	69,995	42,653	352,700	113,700	*Nil.*	943	
10.6.17 to 4.8.17, used by Second and Fifth Armies	7 weeks, Ypres	15,022	147,756	226,790	335,462	24,900	1,415	
24.10.17 to 24.11.17 Used by Third Army	4 weeks, Cambrai	27,637	131,308	90,877	210,924	*Nil.*	330	400 Tank Covers also supplied.

Table IX.

COMPARATIVE OUTPUTS OF CAMOUFLAGE MATERIALS.

Dates.	Period.	Painted.		Garnished Netting.		Road Screening. Sq. yds.	Women Labour at beginning of period.	Remarks.
		Canvas Sheets. Sq. yds.	Scrim. Sq. yds.	Wire. Sq. yds.	Fish. Sq. yds.			
June-Dec., 1916	6 months	300,054	864	176,940	14,305	Nil.	30	
Jan. 1st to 7th, 1917	1 week	878	Nil.	10,620	Nil.	Nil.	} 217	
Jan. to June, 1917	6 months	396,630	182,278	1,139,829	793,390	Nil.		
June 23rd to 30th, 1917	1 week	6,788	10,495	74,760	50,753	Nil.	} 1,079	
June to Dec., 1917	6 months	140,951	1,565,279	1,041,009	2,622,804	112,619		
Dec. 8th to 15th, 1917	1 week	5,580	119,956	41,620	105,855	23,800	} 1,518	
Jan. to May, 1918	5 months	43,993	1,041,421	2,009,755	2,189,957	382,866		
May 22nd to June 6th, 1918 ...	2 weeks	3,303	250,032	230,130	177,806	40,900	1,477	

Table X.

CAMOUFLAGE FACTORY STATISTICAL RETURN.

Wimereux Camouflage Factory. Month ending July, 1918.

FORM C 3.

OUTPUT:

Output	Unit	Qnty.
Painted canvas sheets	sq. yds.	488
Fish netting, garnished	"	177,811
Islands only on wire netting	"	—
" " fish netting	"	—
Scrim sheets	"	200,937
M.G. nets	Nos.	506
Road screening, 6ft.	yds. lin.	—
Wire netting, garnished	sq. yds.	143,460

TOTAL MATERIALS USED:

Material	Unit	Qnty.
Canvas	sq. yds.	194,597
Fish nets	Nos.	1,774
Wire rolls	"	3,731
Scrim	sq. yds.	200,937
Raffia	lbs.	12,348
Coir matting	sq. yds.	—

DETAIL OF LABOUR:

Average Daily Nos.

	Detail	Wom.	Colrd.	Wh.
Fish netting	Tying on knots	100·7		3
	Fixing	10·5		
	Cutting scrim patches	2		1
	Suppling strips	5		
Wire netting	Tying on knots	199·7		2·5
	Cutting scrim patches	5·5		
	Fixing	5		
	Suppling strips	4	4	
	Rolling netting	16		2
	Cutting "			1
M.G. nets	"	40·7		
Canvas	Splitting	3		
	Sewing	12		
	Painting, hand			
	" machine		4	2
	Stripping		15·7	1
Scrim	Painting, hand	14		1
	" machine		11·3	1
Paint	Mixing		4	7·5
Raffia and Scrim Dyeing		8·5	1	1

PAINT AND MEDIUM USED.

Item	Unit	Used
Colours	lbs.	111,326
Boiled oil	gals.	2,445¼
Glue	lbs.	1,3969
Sapon	"	2,445¼
A.P.M.	lbs.	16,868
Formaldehyde	"	317½
Varnish	gals.	—
Stickit	gals.	240¼

DETAIL OF DRY COLOUR USED.

L.B. Green	lbs.	32,984
D.B. Green	"	29,621
Lemon Chrome	"	10,270
Mid Chrome	"	—
Orange Chrome	"	2,536
Burnt Umber	"	5,628
Raw Umber	"	—
Burnt Sienna	"	696
Raw Sienna	"	—
Ultramarine	"	—
Prussian Blue	"	—
Lamp Black	"	1,189
Red Oxide	"	—
Whitening	"	15,242
Terra Alba	"	—
Ochre	"	13,048
C. Blue	"	112

ANALYSIS OF OUTPUT:

		Unit	Qnty.
Total Canvas	Painted	sq. yds.	178,270
	Split	"	194,109
	Stripped	"	194,109
	Dyed	"	—
Total Scrim	Painted, hand	"	55,689
	" machine	"	121,464
	Cut to patches	"	114,344
	Dyed	"	23,522
Total Raffia	Dyed	lbs.	17,808

:: Sq. yds. net.